DISCARD

EX-LIBRIS

W. J. SANDERS

MODERN VERSE

REVISED

Book Two

BY

ANITA P. FORBES

NEW YORK

HENRY HOLT AND COMPANY

CONTENTS

PART ONE

PART TWO

PART THREE

PART FOUR

iv

PART FIVE

PART SIX

PART SEVEN

PART EIGHT

PART NINE

ACKNOWLEDGMENTS

To the following authors, publishers, and individual owners of copyrights our thanks are due for their cooperation in granting formal permission to reprint material.

"American Laughter" by Kenneth A. Robinson is reprinted by permission of the author.

"An Open Boat" (from *The New Morning*) by Alfred Noyes is reprinted by permission of Frederick A. Stokes Company. Canadian rights granted by the author, A. P. Watt and Son, and Messrs. William Blackwood and Sons.

"The Ancient Beautiful Things" by Fanny Stearns Davis is reprinted by permission of the author.

"And the Cock Crew" is reprinted by permission from *The Silver Trumpet* by Amelia Josephine Burr, copyright, 1918, by Doubleday, Doran and Company.

"Answer" (from *Sweet Water and Bitter*) by Virginia Moore is reprinted by permission of Harcourt, Brace and Company, Inc.

"Anthony Crundle" (from *Poems 1908-1919*) by John Drinkwater is reprinted by permission of Houghton Mifflin Company, publishers.

"The Ballad of Nan Bullen" is from *Hill Garden* by Margaret Widdemer, copyright, 1936, and is reprinted by permission of Farrar & Rinehart, Inc.

"Bare Feet" by Dorothy Aldis is reprinted by permission of the author and of *Poetry* (Chicago).

"The Barrel-Organ" (from *Collected Poems*) by Alfred Noyes is reprinted by permission of Frederick A. Stokes Com-

"Coast Cathedral" by Wilbert Snow is reprinted by permission of the author.

"The Code" (from *North of Boston*) by Robert Frost is reprinted by permission of Henry Holt and Company, Inc.

"Continuity" (from *Collected Poems*) by A. E. is reprinted by permission of The Macmillan Company.

"Counter-Attack" (from *Counter-Attack*) by Siegfried Sassoon is reprinted by permission of the author and of E. P. Dutton and Company, publishers. Canadian rights granted by the author.

"Courage" (from *Moods, Songs and Doggerel*) by John Galsworthy is reprinted by permission of Charles Scribner's Sons, publishers.

"The Creation" is reprinted with permission from *God's Trombones* by James Weldon Johnson. Copyright, 1927, by The Viking Press, Inc., New York.

"Crystal Moment" is reprinted from *The Yoke of Thunder* by Robert P. Tristram Coffin, by permission of The Macmillan Company, publishers.

"Da Younga 'Merican" (from *Canzoni*) by T. A. Daly is reprinted by permission of Harcourt, Brace and Company, Inc.

"Death and General Putnam" is taken from *Death and General Putnam and 101 Other Poems,* by Arthur Guiterman, published and copyrighted by E. P. Dutton and Company, Inc., New York.

"Definition" (from *Light of the Years*) by Grace Noll Crowell is reprinted by permission of Harper and Brothers, publishers.

"Does It Matter?" (from *Counter-Attack*) by Siegfried Sassoon is reprinted by permission of the author and of E. P. Dutton and Company, publishers. Canadian rights granted by the author.

"Dulce et Decorum Est" is reprinted with permission from *Poems* by Wilfred Owen, published by The Viking Press,

meyer. Copyright, 1918. Published by The Viking Press, Inc., New York.

"Hills Ruddy with Sumach" (from *Ships and Lovers*) by Thomas Caldecot Chubb is reprinted by permission of Albert and Charles Boni, Inc., publishers.

"The Host of the Air" (from *Collected Poems*) by William Butler Yeats is reprinted by permission of The Macmillan Company, publishers.

"The Horse Thief" (from *The Burglar of the Zodiac*) by William Rose Benét is reprinted by permission of the Yale University Press.

"Idealists" (from *Mushrooms*) by Alfred Kreymborg is reprinted by permission of the author.

"In a Certain Restaurant" (from *Blue Stones*) by Marguerite Wilkinson is reprinted by permission of The Macmillan Company, publishers.

"In Time of 'The Breaking of Nations'" (from *Collected Poems*) by Thomas Hardy is reprinted by permission of The Macmillan Company, publishers.

"In the Cliff Dwellings" (from *Selected Poems*) by Glen Ward Dresbach is reprinted by permission of Henry Holt and Company, Inc.

"Innamorata" (from *The House on the Wold*) by W. Force Stead is reprinted by permission of R. Cobden-Sanderson, Ltd., publishers.

"Irradiations" (III) and "Irradiations" (X) are from *Selected Poems* by John Gould Fletcher, copyright, 1938, and are reprinted by permission of Farrar and Rinehart, Inc.

"Kansas Boy" by Ruth Lechtlitner is reprinted by permission of the author.

"The Kings are Passing Deathward" (from *Ships in Harbour*) by David Morton is reprinted by permission of G. P. Putnam's Sons, publishers.

"La Vie C'est La Vie" by Jessie Redmond Fauset is reprinted by permission of the author and *The Crisis*.

"Lament" is from *Second April* by Edna St. Vincent Millay. Published by Harper and Brothers. Copyright, 1921, by Edna St. Vincent Millay. Reprinted by permission of the author.

"Lavender Lilies" is from *Good Morning, America,* copyright, 1928, by Carl Sandburg. By permission of Harcourt, Brace and Company, Inc.

"Legend" (from *Finders*) by John V. A. Weaver is reprinted by permission of and special arrangement with Alfred A. Knopf, Inc., authorized publishers.

"Leisure" is reprinted from *The Poems of W. H. Davies* (1934) by permission of Jonathan Cape, Ltd. Copyright, 1916, by William H. Davies.

"Lepanto" (from *Collected Poems*) by G. K. Chesterton is used by permission of Dodd, Mead and Company, Inc. Canadian rights granted by A. P. Watt and Son, literary agent to the executrix of the late G. K. Chesterton, and by Messrs. Burnes, Oates and Washbourne.

"The Look" (from *Collected Poems*) by Sara Teasdale is reprinted by permission of The Macmillan Company, publishers.

"A Lynmouth Widow" (from *In Deep Places*) by Amelia Josephine Burr is reprinted by permission of Doubleday, Doran and Company, Inc.

"Man and Dog" is from *Out of Erin,* by Arthur Stringer, copyright, 1911, 1930. Used by special permission of the publishers, The Bobbs-Merrill Company.

"A Man-Child's Lullaby" (from *Poems*) by Brian Hooker is reprinted by permission of the Yale University Press.

"The Man with the Hoe" by Edwin Markham is copyrighted by the author and used by his permission.

"Mother of the World" by Enid Hayward is reprinted by

"The Unseen" is reprinted with permission from *The White Rooster* by George O'Neil, published by Liveright Publishing Corporation.

"When Shakespeare Laughed" (from *The Rocking Horse*) by Christopher Morley is reprinted by permission of the J. B. Lippincott Company, publishers.

"Who Track the Truth" is reprinted with permission from *The Flowering Stone* by George Dillon, copyright, 1931. Published by The Viking Press, Inc., New York.

"Why He Loves Her" by Norman R. Jaffray is reprinted by permission of the author and of *Judge*.

"Wild Strawberries" is reprinted from *Songs of Infancy* by Mary Britton Miller by permission of The Macmillan Company, publishers.

"Wing Harbor" (from *Stone Dust*) by Frank Ernest Hill is reprinted by permission of Longmans, Green and Company.

"Wishes for My Son" (from *The Poetical Works of Thomas MacDonagh*) is used by permission of The Talbot Press (Dublin).

"Work, A Song of Triumph" (from *Gold on Your Pillow*) by Angela Morgan is used by permission of the author.

INTRODUCTION

Color, light, sheen, luster, and sparkle are all around us to-day. Psychologists claim that our spirits rise higher and our achievements are greater for living in surroundings that are brilliant instead of dull. And those practical psychologists, the merchants, constantly stimulate us through the eyes to make us buy more; witness the glitter of a large department store at Christmas time.

Suppose that in passing through the store we stop at the jewelry counter. From glass cases gems glow red, green, blue, purple, yellow, and white in their settings of gold, silver, platinum, and all sorts of shining alloys. Most of the stones are synthetic, marvels of the chemists' skill. We look at a "diamond" pin that appeals to us as a possible gift. At arm's length the effect is well-nigh perfect, at shorter range satisfactory. Not until we peer closely at the piece of jewelry, or turn it this way and that to see how it catches the light, do we miss something.

What is it? Let us ask the clerk to take from its position of honor in the glass case, or from a drawer behind, a real diamond pin or ring. A comparison shows at once why one price tag is perhaps $2.95 and the other $295.50. It is something inside—a leaping fire, an intense glow, almost a mysterious form of life—that distinguishes the genuine. We lay it down with a sigh of appreciation and turn back to buy the imitation that we can afford and that will give us a reasonable amount of pleasure. But we do not forget the real thing.

The more literature, both prose and poetry, that I read, the surer I am that the lasting effect of written expression on the reader is in proportion to the intensity that glows through the author's words. Such intensity comes not merely from the fullness of a writer's emotions, but also from the keenness of his sensations, the depth of his convictions, the height of his aspirations. One or more of these things—a sort of white heat—must shine through to the reader if an author's works are to live. Some of that intensity flares in everyone who voluntarily tries to write; but with most the flare dies down before it becomes a steady glow. Even when the inspiration is fairly sustained, it has to break through the smother of wrong words to find the right ones. Small wonder that comparatively few writers in any generation are what we call "the real thing."

If this yardstick of intensity is the correct measure, the chances of poets to inspire lasting remembrance ought to be greater than the chances of prose writers. Why? Because poetry, being a much more concise form of expression than prose, does not demand such long-sustained intensity. For months, now, a phrase has been running through my head, "the shorthand of beauty." Whether it is my own or whether I may have read it somewhere, it seems to me a fairly good partial definition of poetry. Poetry presents its material through symbols, suggestions, and short cuts. It catches all kinds of emotions, sensations, and ideas at their brief height.

Let us see what some of these are. Below is a poem written by James Elroy Flecker, a poet of the early twentieth century who died tragically young. Read it, particularly the stanza in italics:

TO A POET A THOUSAND YEARS HENCE

I, who am dead a thousand years,
　And wrote this sweet archaic song,
Send you my words for messengers
　The way I shall not pass along.

I care not if you bridge the seas,
  Or ride secure the cruel sky,
Or build consummate palaces
  Of metal or of masonry.

But have you wine and music still,
  And statues and a bright-eyed love,
And foolish thoughts of good and ill,
  And prayers to them who sit above?

How shall we conquer? Like a wind
  That falls at eve our fancies blow,
And old Maeonides the blind
  Said it three thousand years ago.

O friend unseen, unborn, unknown,
  Student of our sweet English tongue,
Read out my words at night, alone,
  I was a poet, I was young.

Since I can never see your face,
  And never shake you by the hand,
I send my soul through time and space
  To greet you. You will understand.

Delight in physical sensation; joy in beautiful things; love;
attempts to reason out good and evil, as shown in life; vague
longings to understand the infinite—what better subjects than
these could there be for poetry throughout the ages? Everybody has experienced them and through experiencing them
has known some of the inner glow that fires the poet. Most
of us cannot put it into words. But a good poet can.

The chief aim of this collection, then, is to show you that
poetry has in it a quality of life which closely touches your
life. The poems included have been carefully measured by the
intensity which they possess, by the degree to which the author

xxiii

makes readers feel or imagine or think about basic human experiences. Almost all the poems have been tried out on twelfth-grade classes of boys and girls for five successive semesters. Of course, not every poem appealed equally to everybody; but every poem impressed at least some pupils as being sincere and forceful.

The secondary aim is to show you a few ways poets have of getting their ideas across to their readers. For this purpose, the collection has been divided into nine parts, in each of which the poems have some resemblance to each other in subject matter. Suggestions are made as to how to study each group for some secrets of poetic technique that are illustrated in different ways by the poems. You can do as much or as little of this as your class and your teacher desire. It is rather fun to turn poems, like diamonds, this way and that, to see different lights on them, and to compare them with others. For fuller comparison, parallel older poems are listed. Just now, you will doubtless find it easier to appreciate the intensity in poems of your own day, because they are written in modern style. But as Flecker put it, "old Maeonides the blind [Homer] said it three thousand years ago." After you have learned to read modern poetry with intelligent appreciation, you will turn back often to some of the older poets. For although their songs may now seem to you hard to understand, before many years you will realize that they wrote about the things that will always lie deepest in human hearts.

A. P. F.

The University School, Pittsburgh, Pa.
Formerly at Weaver High School, Hartford, Conn.

Part One

Life is not life at all without delight.

Patmore

FOREWORD

From the earliest savages to the most recent "jitterbugs" human beings have responded to *rhythm*. Those of us who cannot play musical instruments or sing, tap with our feet or our fingers. All physical movements are easier and more graceful when performed in rhythm; and a pattern in sound gives real pleasure to the ear.

Perhaps because poetry has developed from words chanted to musical accompaniment, poets have always considered rhythm of some sort indispensable. The first realization of what poetry is comes to most readers through its very obvious appeal to the ear. Before you can hear the larger rhythms that flow through groups of lines, you will probably hear the smaller divisions which are called *meters*. The poems in this group illustrate the common English ones. Also you will find here examples of *refrains,* another poetic device inherited from old days. Although refrains are not so frequent as they used to be, they are still effective occasionally for emphasis.

You can easily learn to enjoy the sounds in separate words and in groups of words. Some word-sounds are merely beautiful or strong in themselves, while others are rich in suggestion. In this group of poems, we shall be concerned chiefly with the way in which words fit into metrical and rhythmical effects.

The whole study of what we hear in a poem is fascinating and complicated. Part Six will deal with it more fully. The present point for you is either to read the poems aloud or to listen to them.

LEISURE

What is this life if, full of care,
We have no time to stand and stare?

No time to stand beneath the boughs
And stare as long as sheep or cows.

No time to see when woods we pass,
Where squirrels hide their nuts in grass.

No time to see, in broad daylight,
Streams full of stars, like skies at night.

No time to turn at Beauty's glance,
And watch her feet, how they can dance.

No time to wait till her mouth can
Enrich that smile her eyes began.

A poor life this if, full of care,
We have no time to stand and stare.

W. H. Davies

PLAN FOR A SUMMER DAY

Give me your hand—give me your hand!
Race with me over the yellow sand!
Dive deep into the blue of the sea—
Loose me.

3

Find me again in the warmth of noon,
Love me gaily—leave me soon!
Only a moment can hold such bliss
As this.

But when the sun is folding the day
In fading colors that fade away,
Fold me in sunlight—O my dear,
Draw near!

Draw near against the night, and we
Will play with stars that we may see,
Will play with stars a little while
And smile.

                              Marion Strobel

IN A CERTAIN RESTAURANT

These diners should have sat for old Franz Hals,
For all their faces are as round as moons,
Glowing with jovial warmth and creased with smiles
At the turbulent clatter of many forks and spoons.

There is no music and no cabaret—
China and linen both are coarse and plain—
But food there is, such stout and honest food
As tells a body he has not dined in vain.

Behind a bar three corpulent men in white
Are opening oysters one by one by one,

Laying them delicately on beds of ice,
Friendly and slow, as if they think it fun.

Far back in the room there is a mighty grill
Ruddy with fire, clouded with fragrant steam,
Where ducks and chickens and other gentry turn
Over and over as in a drowsy dream.

And through the air come speeding plates piled high
With giant potatoes, opened, foamy white,
Genial, impressive beefsteaks, lobsters pink
As coral beads, and pastry crisp and light.

This is the place of plenty I like best.
I watch Manhattan burghers and their wives
Eating tremendously, as all men should,
To please their palates and to save their lives.

No finicky fashion, no satiety,
No smirking gesture, and no sour debate
Trouble these diners. They are one with life
Now for a while, though inarticulate.

Such excellent food demands much company:
Oh, to go out with friendly haste and find
The hungriest hungry souls and dine them here—
It would be good to entertain mankind!

Marguerite Wilkinson

WHEN SHAKESPEARE LAUGHED

When Shakespeare laughed, the fun began!
Even the tavern barmaids ran
   To choke in secret, and unbent
   A lace, to ease their merriment.
The *Mermaid* rocked to hear the man.

Then Ben his aching girth would span,
And roar above his pasty pan,
   "Avast there, Will, for I am spent!"
   When Shakespeare laughed.

I' faith, let him be grave who can
   When Falstaff, Puck and Caliban
   In one explosive jest are blent!
   The boatmen on the river lent
An ear to hear the mirthful clan
   When Shakespeare laughed.

Christopher Morley

AMERICAN LAUGHTER

Oh the men who laughed the American laughter
   Whittled their jokes from the tough bull-pines;
They were tall men, sharpened before and after;
   They studied the sky for the weather-signs;
   They tilted their hats and they smoked long-nines!

Their laughter was ladled in Western flagons
  And poured down throats that were parched for more;
This was the laughter of democrat wagons
  And homely men at the cross-roads store
  —It tickled the shawl that a lawyer wore!

It hurt the ears of the dainty and pretty
  But they laughed the louder and laughed their fill,
A laughter made for Virginia City,
  Springfield, and Natchez-under-the-Hill,
  And the river that flows past Hannibal still!

American laughter was lucky laughter,
  A coonskin tune by a homespun bard;
It tasted of hams from the smokehouse rafter
  And locust trees in the courthouse yard,
  And Petroleum Nasby and Artemus Ward!

They laughed at the Mormons and Mike Fink's daughter,
  And the corncob tale of Sut Lovingood's dog,
Till the ague fled from the fever-water
  And the damps deserted the tree-stump bog,
  —They laughed at the tale of the jumping frog!

They laughed at the British, they laughed at Shakers,
  At Horace Greeley and stovepipe hats;
They split their fences and ploughed their acres,
  And treed their troubles like mountain-cats;
  —They laughed calamity out of the flats!

Now the Boston man, according to rumor,
  Said, as he turned in his high-backed bed,

"This doesn't conform to my rules for humor,"
　　And he settled his nightcap over his head,
　　—But it shook the earth like the buffalo-tread!

And the corn grew tall and the fields grew wider,
　　And the land grew sleek with the mirth they sowed;
They laughed the fat meat into the spider,
　　They laughed the blues from the Wilderness Road,
　　—They crossed hard times to the Comstock Lode!

Kenneth Allan Robinson

WORK

A Song of Triumph

Work!
Thank God for the might of it,
The ardor, the urge, the delight of it—
Work that springs from the heart's desire,
Setting the brain and the soul on fire—
Oh, what is so good as the heat of it,
And what is so glad as the beat of it,
And what is so kind as the stern command,
Challenging brain and heart and hand?

Work!
Thank God for the pride of it,
For the beautiful, conquering tide of it,
Sweeping the life in its furious flood,
Thrilling the arteries, cleansing the blood,
Mastering stupor and dull despair,
Moving the dreamer to do and dare.

8

Oh, what is so good as the urge of it,
And what is so glad as the surge of it,
And what is so strong as the summons deep,
Rousing the torpid soul from sleep?

Work!
Thank God for the pace of it,
For the terrible, keen, swift race of it;
Fiery steeds in full control,
Nostrils a-quiver to greet the goal,
Work, the Power that drives behind,
Guiding the purposes, taming the mind,
Holding the runaway wishes back,
Reining the will to one steady track,
Speeding the energies faster, faster,
Triumphing over disaster.
Oh, what is so good as the pain of it,
And what is so great as the gain of it?
And what is so kind as the cruel goad,
Forcing us on through the rugged road?

Work!
Thank God for the swing of it,
For the clamoring, hammering ring of it,
Passion of labor daily hurled
On the mighty anvils of the world.
Oh, what is so fierce as the flame of it?
And what is so huge as the aim of it?
Thundering on through dearth and doubt,
Calling the plan of the Maker out.
Work, the Titan; Work, the friend,
Shaping the earth to a glorious end,

9

Draining the swamps and blasting the hills,
Doing whatever the Spirit wills—
Rending a continent apart,
To answer the dream of the Master heart.
Thank God for a world where none may shirk—
Thank God for the splendor of work!

Angela Morgan

THE FEET OF THE YOUNG MEN

1897

Now the Four-way Lodge is opened, now the Hunting
    Winds are loose—
  Now the Smokes of Spring go up to clear the brain;
Now the Young Men's hearts are troubled for the whis-
    per of the Trues,
  Now the Red Gods make their medicine again!
Who hath seen the beaver busied? Who hath watched
    the black-tail mating?
  Who hath lain alone to hear the wild-goose cry?
Who hath worked the chosen water where the ouananiche
    is waiting
  Or the sea-trout's jumping-crazy for the fly?

He must go—go—go away from here!
  On the other side the world he's overdue.
'Send your road is clear before you when the old Spring-
    fret comes o'er you,
And the Red Gods call for you!

So for one the wet sail arching through the rainbow
    round the bow,
    And for one the creak of snow-shoes on the crust;
And for one the lakeside lilies where the bull-moose waits
    the cow,
    And for one the mule-train coughing in the dust.
Who hath smelt wood-smoke at twilight? Who hath
    heard the birch-log burning?
    Who is quick to read the noises of the night?
Let him follow with the others, for the Young Men's feet
    are turning
    To the camps of proved desire and known delight!

Let him go—go—go away from here!
    On the other side the world he's overdue.
'Send your road is clear before you when the old Spring-
    fret comes o'er you,
And the Red Gods call for you!

I

Do you know the blackened timber—do you know that
    racing stream
    With the raw, right-angled log-jam at the end;
And the bar of sun-warmed shingle where a man may
    bask and dream
    To the click of shod canoe-poles round the bend?
It is there that we are going with our rods and reels and
    traces,
    To a silent, smoky Indian that we know—
To a couch of new-pulled hemlock, with the starlight on
    our faces,
    For the Red Gods call us out and we must go!

They must go—go—go away from here!
  On the other side the world they're overdue.
'Send your road is clear before you when the old Spring-
    fret comes o'er you,
And the Red Gods call for you!

II

Do you know the shallow Baltic where the seas are steep
    and short,
  Where the bluff, lee-boarded fishing-luggers ride?
Do you know the joy of threshing leagues to leeward of
    your port
  On a coast you've lost the chart of overside?
It is there that I am going, with an extra hand to bale
    her—
  Just one able 'long-shore loafer that I know.
He can take his chance of drowning, while I sail and sail
    and sail her,
  For the Red Gods call me out and I must go!

He must go—go—go away from here!
  On the other side the world he's overdue.
'Send your road is clear before you when the old Spring-
    fret comes o'er you,
And the Red Gods call for you!

III

Do you know the pile-built village where the sago-dealers
    trade—
  Do you know the reek of fish and wet bamboo?

Do you know the steaming stillness of the orchid-scented
    glade
  When the blazoned, bird-winged butterflies flap
    through?
It is there that I am going with my camphor, net and
    boxes,
  To a gentle, yellow pirate that I know—
To my little wailing lemurs, to my palms and flying-
    foxes,
  For the Red Gods call me out and I must go!

He must go—go—go away from here!
  On the other side the world he's overdue.
'Send your road is clear before you when the old Spring-
  fret comes o'er you,
And the Red Gods call for you!

IV

Do you know the world's white roof-tree—do you know
    that windy rift
  Where the baffling mountain-eddies chop and change?
Do you know the long day's patience, belly-down on
    frozen drift,
  While the head of heads is feeding out of range?
It is there that I am going, where the boulders and the
    snow lie,
  With a trusty, nimble tracker that I know.
I have sworn an oath, to keep it on the Horns of Ovis
    Poli,
  And the Red Gods call me out and I must go!

He must go—go—go away from here!
  On the other side the world he's overdue.
'Send your road is clear before you when the old Spring-
    fret comes o'er you,
And the Red Gods call for you!

Now the Four-way Lodge is opened—now the Smokes of
    Council rise—
  Pleasant smokes, ere yet 'twixt trail and trail they
    choose—
Now the girths and ropes are tested: now they pack their
    last supplies:
  Now our Young Men go to dance before the Trues!
Who shall meet them at those altars—who shall light
    them to that shrine?
  Velvet-footed, who shall guide them to their goal?
Unto each the voice and vision: unto each his spoor and
    sign—
Lonely mountain in the Northland, misty sweat-bath
    'neath the Line—
  And to each a man that knows his naked soul!
White or yellow, black or copper, he is waiting, as a
    lover,
  Smoke of funnel, dust of hooves, or beat of train—
Where the high grass hides the horseman or the glaring
    flats discover—
Where the steamer hails the landing, or the surf-boat
    brings the rover—
Where the rails run out in sand-drift . . . Quick! ah
    heave the camp-kit over,
For the Red Gods make their medicine again!

14

And we go—go—go away from here!
  On the other side the world we're overdue!
'Send the road is clear before you when the old Spring-
    fret comes o'er you,
And the Red Gods call for you!

Rudyard Kipling

FOLLOW, FOLLOW, FOLLOW

Follow! Follow!! Follow!
Blackbird, thrush and swallow!
The air is soft, the sun is dancing through
The dancing boughs;
A little while me company along
And I will go with you.
Arouse! Arouse!
Among the leaves I sing my pleasant song.

Sky! Sky! On high! Oh gentle majesty!
Come all ye happy birds and follow, follow!
Under the slender interlacing boughs,
Blackbird and thrush and swallow!
No longer in the sunlight sit and drowse
But me accompany along;
No longer be ye mute!
Arouse! Arouse!
Among the leaves I sing my pleasant song.

Lift, lift, ye happy birds! Lift song and wing;
And sing and fly; and fly again, and sing

Up to the very blueness of the sky
Your happy words!
O Follow! Follow! Follow!
Where we go racing through the shady ways,
Blackbird, thrush and swallow,
Shouting aloud our ecstasy of praise!
Under the slender interlacing boughs
Me company along;
The sun is coming with us!
Rouse! O Rouse!
Among the leaves I sing my pleasant song.

James Stephens

ROMANCE

When I was but thirteen or so
   I went into a golden land,
Chimborazo, Cotopaxi
   Took me by the hand.

My father died, my brother too,
   They passed like fleeting dreams,
I stood where Popocatapetl
   In the sunlight gleams.

I dimly heard the master's voice
   And boys far-off at play,
Chimborazo, Cotopaxi
   Had stolen me away.

16

I walked in a great golden dream
  The town streets, to and fro—
Shining Popocatapetl
  Gleamed with his cap of snow.

I walked home with a gold dark boy
  And never a word I'd say,
Chimborazo, Cotopaxi
  Had taken my speech away;

I gazed entranced upon his face
  Fairer than any flower—
O shining Popocatapetl,
  It was thy magic hour;

The houses, people, traffic seemed
  Thin fading dreams by day,
Chimborazo, Cotopaxi,
  They had stolen my soul away!

                    W. J. Turner

SONG

"Oh! Love," they said, "is King of Kings,
  And Triumph is his crown.
Earth fades in flame before his wings,
  And Sun and Moon bow down."—
But that, I knew, would never do;
  And Heaven is all too high.
So whenever I meet a Queen, I said,
  I will not catch her eye.

17

"Oh! Love," they said, and "Love," they said,
　"The gift of Love is this;
A crown of thorns about thy head,
　And vinegar to thy kiss!"
But Tragedy is not for me;
　And I'm content to be gay.
So whenever I spied a Tragic Lady,
　I went another way.

And so I never feared to see
　You wander down the street,
Or come across the fields to me
　On ordinary feet.
For what they'd never told me of,
　And what I never knew;
It was that all the time, my love,
　Love would be merely you.

Rupert Brooke

WISHES FOR MY SON

(Born on St. Cecilia's Day, 1912)

Now, my son, is life for you,
And I wish you joy of it,—
Joy of power in all you do,
Deeper passion, better wit
Than I had who had enough,
Quicker life and length thereof,
More of every gift but love.

Love I have beyond all men,
Love that now you share with me—
What have I to wish you then
But that you be good and free,
And that God to you may give
Grace in stronger days to live?

For I wish you more than I
Ever knew of glorious deed,
Though no rapture passed me by
That an eager heart could heed,
Though I followed heights and sought
Things the sequel never brought:

Wild and perilous holy things
Flaming with a martyr's blood,
And the joy that laughs and sings
Where a foe must be withstood,
Joy of headlong happy chance
Leading on the battle dance.

But I found no enemy,
No man in a world of wrong,
That Christ's word of charity
Did not render clean and strong—
Who was I to judge my kind,
Blindest groper of the blind?

God to you may give the sight
And the clear undoubting strength,
Wars to knit for single right,
Freedom's war to knit at length,

And to win, through wrath and strife,
To the sequel of my life.

But for you, so small and young,
Born on St. Cecilia's Day,
I in more harmonious song
Now for nearer joys should pray—
Simple joys: the natural growth
Of your childhood and your youth,
Courage, innocence, and truth:

These for you, so small and young,
In your hand and heart and tongue.

Thomas MacDonagh

ANTHONY CRUNDLE

Here lies the body of
ANTHONY CRUNDLE
Farmer, of this parish,
Who died in 1849 at the age of 82.
"He delighted in music."
R. I. P.
And of
SUSAN,
For fifty-three years his wife.
Who died in 1860, aged 86.

Anthony Crundle of Dorrington Wood
Played on a piccolo. Lord was he,
For seventy years, of sheaves that stood
Under the perry and cider tree;
Anthony Crundle, R. I. P.

20

And because he prospered with sickle and scythe,
  With cattle afield and labouring ewe,
Anthony was uncommonly blithe,
  And played of a night to himself and Sue;
  Anthony Crundle, 82.

The earth to till, and a tune to play,
  And Susan for fifty years and three,
And Dorrington Wood at the end of day. . . .
  May Providence do no worse by me;
  Anthony Crundle, R. I. P.

                                    John Drinkwater

THE ANCIENT BEAUTIFUL THINGS

I am all alone in the room.
The evening stretches before me
Like a road all delicate gloom
Till it reaches the midnight's gate.
And I hear his step on the path,
And his questioning whistle, low
At the door as I hurry to meet him.

He will ask, "Are the doors all locked?
Is the fire made safe on the hearth?
And she—is she sound asleep?"

I shall say, "Yes, the doors are locked,
And the ashes are white as the frost:
Only a few red eyes
To stare at the empty room.
And she is all sound asleep,

21

Up there where the silence sings,
And the curtains stir in the cold."

He will ask, "And what did you do
While I have been gone so long?
So long! Four hours or five!"

I shall say, "There was nothing I did.—
I mended that sleeve of your coat.
And I made her a little white hood
Of the furry pieces I found
Up in the garret to-day.
She shall wear it to play in the snow,
Like a little white bear,—and shall laugh,
And tumble, and crystals of stars
Shall shine on her cheeks and hair.
—It was nothing I did.—I thought
You would never come home again!"

Then he will laugh out, low,
Being fond of my folly, perhaps;
And softly and hand in hand
We shall creep upstairs in the dusk
To look at her, lying asleep:
Our little gold bird in her nest:
The wonderful bird who flew in
At the window our life flung wide.
(How should we have chosen her,
Had we seen them all in a row,
The unborn vague little souls,
All wings and tremulous hands?
How should we have chosen her,

22

Made like a star to shine,
Made like a bird to fly,
Out of a drop of our blood,
And earth, and fire, and God?)

Then we shall go to sleep,
Glad.—
        O God, did you know
When you molded men out of clay,
Urging them up and up
Through the endless circles of change,
Travail and turmoil and death,
Many would curse you down,
Many would live all gray
With their faces flat like a mask:
But there would be some, O God,
Crying to you each night,
"I am so glad! so glad!
I am so rich and gay!
How shall I thank you, God?"

Was that one thing you knew
When you smiled and found it was good:
The curious teeming earth
That grew like a child at your hand?
Ah, you might smile, for that!—

—I am all alone in the room.
The books and the pictures peer,
Dumb old friends, from the dark.
The wind goes high on the hills,
And my fire leaps out, being proud.
The terrier, down on the hearth,

Twitches and barks in his sleep,
Soft little foolish barks,
More like a dream than a dog . . .
I will mend the sleeve of that coat,
All ragged,—and make her the hood
Furry, and white, for the snow.
She shall tumble and laugh . . .

                    Oh, I think
Though a thousand rivers of grief
Flood over my head—though a hill
Of horror lie on my breast,—
Something will sing, "Be glad!
You have had all your heart's desire:
The unknown things that you asked
When you lay awake in the nights,
Alone, and searching the dark
For the secret wonder of life.
You have had them (can you forget?):
The ancient beautiful things!" . . .

How long he is gone. And yet
It is only an hour or two . . .

Oh, I am so happy. My eyes
Are troubled with tears.
                Did you know,
O God, they would be like this,
Your ancient beautiful things?
Are there more?   Are there more,—out there?—
O God, are there always more?

                    Fannie Stearns Davis

PART ONE

QUESTIONS AND SUGGESTIONS

Leisure

Since this poem is about quiet, contemplative happiness, you would not expect that it should be read fast. Two things about the way it is written "slow it down." What are they?

Try having this read aloud by five people—all five reading the first and last stanzas and one reading each stanza between.

Plan for a Summer Day

Read aloud the first four lines of this and then the first two couplets of "Leisure." Why is the movement as different as the moods which the words suggest?

Within this poem itself the mood changes somewhat. How is this indicated by the movement and sound of the lines in the first and the fourth stanzas?

In a Certain Restaurant

How many accents are there in each line of this? (Only three other poems in the group have more than four.) You see, the reader is meant to get the impression of something heavier, more deliberate.

Read these lines aloud for their sound:

"At the turbulent clatter of many forks and spoons"
"Are opening oysters one by one by one"
"Over and over as in a drowsy dream"

25

When Shakespeare Laughed

Which lines do you think most successfully combine a picture with the very sound of laughter? Does the picture remind you of any in the previous poem? Does the sound?

The difficult verse form chosen by Morley requires that there be only three syllable sounds in the rhyme positions, and that these be placed in a certain order within the fifteen lines. Are any words forced into the rhyme pattern?

American Laughter

The very word "laughter" has a broad, gay sound; that is probably why Robinson repeated it in all stanzas but one. Read that one aloud, listening to hear what a finicky, pinched effect is gained from the words used. How does it fit the subject matter?

This is the first poem you have had which makes frequent use of a three-syllable foot; that is, it puts two unaccented syllables between an accented syllable and the next accented one. Notice how very different the movement is from that in "Leisure," where unaccented and accented syllables alternate throughout.

Work, A Song of Triumph

The American pioneers made their work fun; perhaps that was one reason why they accomplished great things. What two other attitudes toward work are stressed here?

In the rhymes, what is different from anything you have had in the poems so far? What effect does it have upon the reading of the lines? (See Reference List, "Rhyme.")

The Feet of the Young Men

Like Turner, the author of *Romance*, Kipling was born in a far corner of the world—India. But by the time he wrote this poem, he had seen all the places of which he speaks. What makes the poem sound brisk and energetic?

Judging from this poem, what is the use of a refrain? Try reading it in chorus, the stanzas being read solo.

Follow, Follow, Follow

Why do most of us sing when we are out hiking on a lovely day? Why do we run rather than walk, at times? Can you fancy that all nature is happy, too?

What is the effect of having short lines mixed with long?

If a poem is to have a refrain, should it have stanzas of regular length?

Romance

Have you ever been struck by the rhythm of names—your own, other people's, place-names? It may have been the beautiful sound of these queer-looking South American names that aroused the interest of a boy born and brought up in Australia. The oftener he repeated them, perhaps, the more he could fancy himself within sight of huge, snow-capped volcanoes such as he had never seen.

Read the poem rather slowly, in a sort of chant. (The three names are pronounced Chĭm-bŏ-rä′zō, Kō-tŏ-păk′sē, Pŏ-pō′kä-tā′pĕt'l.

An English poet outstanding for his skill in weaving proper names into poetry is Milton.

Song

This title suggests that the poem might be set to music. If you did make a setting, would you keep the same key and the same tempo throughout, or vary them? Would the words lend themselves to musical sounds? the sentences to musical phrasing?

The meter is the same as that of the old English ballads, although they were usually grouped in four-line stanzas. How many accents are there in alternate lines?

27

Wishes for My Son

The quality of character chiefly stressed as a wish for the child is stronger than any other expressed in this group. What is it? Does the sound of the verse bring it out? Should you want to set this poem to music?

Anthony Crundle

Drinkwater probably had two reasons for prefacing this poem by the actual epitaph seen in the Dorrington Wood churchyard. One of them you can hear, if you read the whole thing aloud.

Why did he choose a rather regular rhythm for the lines? Why did he use very simple words?

From the very brief suggestions of what gave this farmer happiness, could you write a longer poem of your own about one scene—say, the one where he "played of a night to himself and Sue"?

The Ancient Beautiful Things

What are the "ancient beautiful things," as presented in this poem? Considering them as sources of happiness, how do they compare with the sources behind other poems in this group?

The sound effects here are unusual in two ways: the shortness of the lines throughout, and something that takes the place of rhymes at the end of lines in most cases.

Say the words in the following pairs one after the other: locked, frost; perhaps, hand; wide, shine; think, hill. They illustrate an effect called *assonance*. Can you define it from these examples? Find other examples in the poem.

PART ONE

SUGGESTED SUPPLEMENTARY READING

Older Poems

The Happy Heart	Thomas Dekker
Fortunati Nimium . . .	Thomas Campion
Character of a Happy Life .	Henry Wotton
Solitude	Alexander Pope
The Cotter's Saturday Night .	Robert Burns
The Barefoot Boy . . .	John Greenleaf Whittier
A Winter Wish . . .	Robert Hinchley Messinger
Give Me the Splendid Silent Sun .	Walt Whitman
"I taste a liquor never brewed" .	Emily Dickinson

Newer Poems

Song of the Thrush . . .	T. A. Daly
The Three O'Clock Shift .	W. W. Gibson
Brother Fidelis	Gwen Upcott
Sicilian Emigrant's Song .	William Carlos Williams
Happiness Betrays Me . .	Helen Hoyt
Snatch of Sliphorn Jazz . .	Carl Sandburg
A Song of Happiness . .	Ernest Rhys
Echoes of Childhood . .	Alice Corbin Henderson

Part Two

The present is big with the future.

Leibnitz

FOREWORD

Have you ever seen electric sparks leap between two ends of wire? You might think of a poet as "positive" and yourself as "negative" and the sparks which fuse in a flash of blinding beauty as your imaginations leaping out to meet each other when you read his poem.

"But I'm no good at imagining things," you may protest. That may be true now; but it need not be true always. The chief question is whether you want to use your imagination. If you do you can encourage and train your imagination to a surprising extent, just as you can learn a sport or acquire an accomplishment. Try reading the poems in this group with that "want-to" attitude. They are fairly simple pictures of modern scenes and people in which the poets have implied more than they have expressed. Sometimes the implication is the chief point of a poem.

Those of you who have been gifted with imaginations usually like poetry. You can help the others very much by reading the poems aloud while they listen, for your own ability to see behind the lines will carry through your reading. Not everyone else, of course, will see the same things that you do; a poem says something slightly different to everyone. But that's the fun of it.

A BOOK ON ECONOMICS

Between long rows of figures lurk
Pictures of little boys at work.

And how poor women fade away
Page after page the margins say.

And in a note once in a while
I see death freeze a baby's smile.

Haniel Long

SEARED

> "I can't spend money," he said,
> "It takes a piece out of my heart."

Sixty years it rode me like a horse;
It whipped me, I trembled:
Ten lifetimes I worked for it
Penny by penny in the tin box
Under the loose board in the floor.

They lifted me high to the table:
I was so little they laughed at me
And said, "Moscha will be a boss some day."
Cross legged I sat proud and my mother cried,
"God help him his hands are stiff with cold."
A woolen shawl they wrapped around my legs.
The red eye of the oil stove looked angry,
And the smell of oil was in the room.

Always I slept in the thick air
And always they shook me, "Wake up, little boss,"
Always the pants piled high;
And always my father looked over his glasses
A little black cap on his head,
Saying, "Save your pennies, Moscha,
A man must have money. Sickness comes,
Death comes, God forbid. A man must have money."

Death came. My father's place was empty at the table,
My mother's eyes were red with weeping.
And always the pants piled to the roof.
And always sickness and death. Always the cry
"Where will the money come from?"
Oh the money was like the light in the temple
That must not go out.
And all around the blackness of the poor ones
The old ones who ask in the streets
With their hands out.
And the money was pressed like blood
From my finger-tips.

Yes, I have money now. . . . I say to my sister
Buy what we must . . . leave me alone.
I can't spend money;
It takes a piece out of my heart.

                                        Helen Salz

BOY WITH HIS HAIR CUT SHORT

Sunday shuts down on this twentieth-century evening.
The L passes. Twilight and bulb define
the brown room, the overstuffed plush sofa,
the boy, and the girl's thin hands above his head.
A neighbor radio sings stock news, serenade.

He sits at the table, head down, the young clear neck ex-
　　posed,
watching the drugstore sign from the tail of his eye;
tattoo, neon, until the eye blears, while his
solicitous tall sister, simple in blue, bending
behind him, cuts his hair with her cheap shears.

The arrow's electric red always reaches its mark,
successful neon! He coughs, impressed by that precision.
His child's forehead, forever protected by his cap,
is bleached against the lamplight as he turns head
and steadies to let the snippets drop.

Erasing the failure of weeks with level fingers,
she sleeks the fine hair, combing: "You'll look fine to-
　　morrow!
You'll surely find something, they can't keep turning you
　　down;
the finest gentleman's not so trim as you!" Smiling, he
　　raises
the adolescent forehead wrinkling ironic now.

He sees his decent suit laid out, new-pressed,
his carfare on the shelf. He lets his head fall, meeting

her earnest hopeless look, seeing the sharp blades split-
    ting,
the darkened room, the impersonal sign, her motion,
the blue vein, bright on her temple, pitifully beating.

Muriel Rukeyser

THE CODE

There were three in the meadow by the brook
Gathering up windrows, piling cocks of hay,
With an eye always lifted toward the west
Where an irregular sun-bordered cloud
Darkly advanced with a perpetual dagger
Flickering across its bosom.   Suddenly
One helper, thrusting pitchfork in the ground,
Marched himself off the field and home.   One stayed.
The town-bred farmer failed to understand.

"What is there wrong?"

                        "Something you just now said."

"What did I say?"

                    "About our taking pains."

"To cock the hay?—because it's going to shower?
I said that more than half an hour ago.
I said it to myself as much as you."

"You didn't know.   But James is one big fool.
He thought you meant to find fault with his work.
That's what the average farmer would have meant.
James would take time, of course, to chew it over
Before he acted: he's just got round to act."

"He is a fool if that's the way he takes me."

"Don't let it bother you.   You've found out something.
The hand that knows his business won't be told
To do work better or faster—those two things.
I'm as particular as anyone:
Most likely I'd have served you just the same.
But I know you don't understand our ways.
You were just talking what was in your mind,
What was in all our minds, and you weren't hinting.
Tell you a story of what happened once:
I was up here in Salem at a man's
Named Sanders with a gang of four or five
Doing the haying.   No one liked the boss.
He was one of the kind sports call a spider,
All wiry arms and legs that spread out wavy
From a humped body nigh as big's a biscuit.
But work! that man could work, especially
If by so doing he could get more work
Out of his hired help.   I'm not denying
He was hard on himself.   I couldn't find
That he kept any hours—not for himself.
Daylight and lantern-light were one to him:
I've heard him pounding in the barn all night.
But what he liked was someone to encourage.
Them that he couldn't lead he'd get behind

And drive, the way you can, you know, in mowing—
Keep at their heels and threaten to mow their legs off.
I'd seen about enough of his bulling tricks
(We call that bulling). I'd been watching him.
So when he paired off with me in the hayfield
To load the load, thinks I, Look out for trouble.
I built the load and topped it off; old Sanders
Combed it down with a rake and says, 'O.K.'
Everything went well till we reached the barn
With a big catch to empty in a bay.
You understand that meant the easy job
For the man up on top of throwing *down*
The hay and rolling it off wholesale,
Where on a mow it would have been slow lifting.
You wouldn't think a fellow'd need much urging
Under these circumstances, would you now?
But the old fool seizes his fork in both hands,
And looking up bewhiskered out of the pit,
Shouts like an army captain, 'Let her come!'
Thinks I, D'ye mean it? 'What was that you said?'
I asked out loud, so's there'd be no mistake,
'Did you say, Let her come?' 'Yes, let her come.'
He said it over, but he said it softer.
Never you say a thing like that to a man,
Not if he values what he is. God, I'd as soon
Murdered him as left out his middle name.
I'd built the load and knew right where to find it.
Two or three forkfuls I picked lightly round for
Like meditating, and then I just dug in
And dumped the rackful on him in ten lots.
I looked over the side once in the dust

And caught sight of him treading-water-like,
Keeping his head above. 'Damn ye,' I says,
'That gets ye!' He squeaked like a squeezed rat.
That was the last I saw or heard of him.
I cleaned the rack and drove out to cool off.
As I sat mopping hayseed from my neck,
And sort of waiting to be asked about it,
One of the boys sings out, 'Where's the old man?'
'I left him in the barn under the hay.
If ye want him, ye can go and dig him out.'
They realized from the way I swobbed my neck
More than was needed something must be up.
They headed for the barn; I stayed where I was.
They told me afterward. First they forked hay,
A lot of it, out into the barn floor.
Nothing! They listened for him. Not a rustle.
I guess they thought I'd spiked him in the temple
Before I buried him, or I couldn't have managed.
They excavated more. 'Go keep his wife
Out of the barn.' Someone looked in a window.
And curse me if he wasn't in the kitchen
Slumped way down in a chair, with both his feet
Stuck in the oven, the hottest day that summer.
He looked so clean disgusted from behind
There was no one that dared to stir him up,
Or let him know that he was being looked at.
Apparently I hadn't buried him
(I may have knocked him down); but my just trying
To bury him had hurt his dignity.
He had gone to the house so's not to meet me.
He kept away from us all afternoon.

39

We tended to his hay. We saw him out
After a while picking peas in his garden:
He couldn't keep away from doing something."

"Weren't you relieved to find he wasn't dead?"

"No! and yet I don't know—it's hard to say.
I went about to kill him fair enough."

"You took an awkward way. Did he discharge you?"

"Discharge me? No! He knew I did just right."

Robert Frost

THE PYLONS

The secret of these hills was stone, and cottages
Of that stone made,
And crumbling roads
That turned on sudden hidden villages.

Now over these small hills they have built the concrete
That trails black wire:
Pylons, those pillars
Bare like nude, giant girls that have no secret.

The valley with its gilt and evening look
And the green chestnut
Of customary root
Are mocked dry like the parched bed of a brook.

40

But far above and far as sight endures
Like whips of anger
With lightning's danger
There runs the quick perspective of the future.

This dwarfs our emerald country by its trek
So tall with prophecy:
Dreaming of cities
Where often clouds shall lean their swan-white neck.

Stephen Spender

WING HARBOR

Motors, like men, will stop for little things;
He should have pulled the air valve, pulled the choke;
The booming of the pistons dragged and broke—
He was alone with sky and hissing wings.

Swiftly he nursed the engine, could not rouse
More than a cough. . . . Below he glimpsed a town.
He'd have to choose a field and set her down. . . .
They said the safest place was one with cows. . . .

Descending in a whispering, shallow arc
He saw the sun halved by the mounting earth;
A thin, high moon came whitening into birth,
Shadows across the fields fell long and dark.

Beneath him cubes of house and barn and stack
In the clear glow were toys his hand could seize;

A pond's green eye shone jewelled in black trees;
A pigmy train slid soundless down its track.

Yet this simplicity was a bright mask
That shut the face and soul from peering eyes;
These silent toys would swell to sound and size
Like shapes unbottled from a magic flask;

Far down the slanting air this gilded town
Caught unaware with wonder at his wings,
Would speak to him surprised and secret things,
As to a sudden god come sweeping down.

He felt its promise like a boy aglow
In a dim theater, who waits to see
A blur of light, and curtains noiselessly
Shed back to let a centre shine and grow;

Down then, surprise the gleam with sudden hand!
While lads about his wings mouth-gaping walk,
And aproned women stand and old men talk,
And a girl's laugh comes light from the dark land. . . .

He closed the long arc in a downward bank
And dove through whine of wires and mouthing wind;
Earth's earth, for hours of soaring left behind,
Rushed back as if from hiding as he sank.

Trees bounded up like giants out of caves,
Houses grown high again flashed ruddy light,
Men sent once more their voices on the night
Like ghosts sprung fleshed, and speaking out of graves.

Then idly, habit-chained, his fingers found
And shook the throttle. Swift as a hurtling knife
The motor wrenched from death to booming life
And ripped his mood with jagged points of sound.

Amazed he heard it crash, felt churning air
Upshoulder him. He thought, "Who'll know or tell?
I'll set her down. The mail can go to hell";
He thought again, "An hour'll get me there."

He could not stop. The dream on which he fed
Took the sharp brunt of sound and seemed to fly
In broken bits; the ship pulled toward the sky
And drew him up, confused, discomfited;

The motor roared, he mounted in a zoom,
Women in doorways stared, dogs leapt about,
A boy pursued his dust with voiceless shout;
The town sank back to points of light in gloom.

The 'plane tore on and up, it leapt and tossed
Like lightning jolted from the black of rain;
He pushed the throttle, shook the stick, to gain
Sense of command bewilderingly lost.

Vainly. He was not god now, was not free,
Throttle and stick and bar were no avail;
He felt like someone on a comet's tail
Making grotesque pretense of mastery.

He watched the valve springs, black against the sky,
Play on relentlessly; he felt the night

Go streaming past his face with jeer and bite;
The motor seemed to drown him in its cry.

He thought of gods who flew from star to star;
He thought of men who move on wheels and wings,
Masters and mastered in a world of things
Builded too little by them—or too far.

Frank Ernest Hill

BROADWAY

How like the stars are these white, nameless faces!
    These far innumerable burning coals!
This pale procession out of stellar spaces,
    This Milky Way of souls!
Each in its own bright nebulae enfurled,
Each face, dear God, a world!

I fling my gaze out through the silent night—
    In those far stars, what gardens, what high halls,
Has mortal yearning built for its delight,
    What chasms and what walls?
What quiet mansions where a soul may dwell?
What Heaven and what Hell?

Hermann Hagedorn

LEGEND

I wonder where it could of went to;
   I know I seen it just as plain:
A beautiful, big fairy city
   Shinin' through the rain.

Rain it was, not snow—in winter!
   Special-order April weather
Ticklin' at our two faces
   Pressed up close together.

Not a single soul was near us
   Standin' out there on the bow;
When we passed another ferry
   He says, sudden, "Now!"

Then I looked where he was pointin'. . . .
   I seen a magic city rise. . . .
Gleamin' windows, like when fields is
   Full of fireflies.

Towers and palaces in the clouds, like,
   Real as real, but nice and blurred.
"Oh!"—I starts in—but he wispers
   "Hush! Don't say a word!

"Don't look long, and don't ast questions,
   Elset you make the fairies sore.
They won't let you even see it
   Never any more.

"Don't you try to ever go there—
  It's to dream of, not to find.
Lovely things like that is always
  Mostly in your mind."

Somethin' made me say, "It's Jersey!" . . .
  Somethin' mean. . . . He hollers, "Hell!"
Now you done it, sure as shootin',
  Now you bust the spell!"

Sure enough, the towers and castles
  Went like lightnin' out of sight. . . .
Nothin' there but filthy Jersey
  On a drizzly night.

John V. A. Weaver

IRRADIATIONS

III

In the gray skirts of the fog seamews skirl desolately,
And flick like bits of paper propelled by a wind
About the flabby sails of a departing ship
Crawling slowly down the low reaches
Of the river.
About the keel there is a bubbling and gurgling
Of grumpy water;
And as the prow noses out a way for itself,
It seems to weave a dream of bubbles and flashing foam,
A dream of strange islands whereto it is bound:

46

Pearl islands drenched with the dawn.
The palms flash under the immense dark sky,
Down which the sun dives to embrace the earth:
Drums boom and conches bray,
And with a crash of crimson cymbals
Suddenly appears above the polished backs of slaves
A king in a breastplate of gold
Gigantic
Amid tossed roses and swaying dancers
That melt into pale undulations and muffled echoes
'Mid the bubbling of the muddy water,
And the swirling of the seamews above the sullen river.

John Gould Fletcher

EEN NAPOLI

Here een Noo Yorka, where am I
Seence I am landa las' July,
All gray an' ogly ees da sky,
    An' cold as eet can be.
But steell so long I maka mon',
So long ees worka to be done,
I can forgat how shines da sun
    Een Napoli.

But oh, w'en pass da boy dat sal
Da violets, an' I can smal
How sweet dey are, I can not tal
    How seeck my heart ees be.

47

I no can work, how mooch I try,
But only seet an' wondra why
I could not justa leeve an' die
    Een Napoli.

        T. A. Daly

ROSES IN THE SUBWAY

A wan-cheeked girl with faded eyes
    Came stumbling down the crowded car,
Clutching her burden to her breast
    As though she held a star.

Roses, I swear it! Red and sweet
    And struggling from her pinched white hands,
Roses . . . like captured hostages
    From far and fairy lands!

The thunder of the rushing train
    Was like a hush. . . . The flower scent
Breathed faintly on the stale, whirled air
    Like some dim sacrament—

I saw a garden stretching out
    And morning on it like a crown—
And o'er a bed of crimson bloom
    My mother . . . stooping down.

        Dana Burnet

THE RIVETER

(For Gustave Davidson)

The steam-shovels had sunk their teeth
   Through earth and rock until a hole
Yawned like a black hell underneath,
   Like a coal-crater with all the coal
Torn out of her: the shovels bit
The stinking stony broth—and spit.

The Wops went up and down; they spilled
   Cement like a groggy soup in chutes;
They mixed the mortar and they filled
   The gash with it. . . . Short swarthy brutes
They were, who reeked of rock and wet
Lime and accumulated sweat.

At first the work was tame enough:
   Only another foundation like
Hundreds before and just as tough
   To stand under a ten-ton spike.
But it was different when a whir
Of steel announced the riveter.

One long lad of them took the crowd
   As he straddled the girders and hooked the nuts
Livid-white hot: and we allowed
   He was the lunatic for guts;
The sidewalk bleachers yelled as he
Speared a sizzler dizzily.

They got to call him the "Rivet Ruth"—
   That crisp corn shock of gusty hair,

49

That blue hawk-eye and devil of youth
  Juggling with death on a treacherous stair,
Tipping his heart on a beam of steel
That made his pavement audience reel.

The riveting hammers stuttered and kicked;
  The ten-ton trestles whined in the winch;
And still this golden Icarus picked
  The hissing rivets by half an inch,
Twirled and nailed them on the spin
Out of the air and rocked them in.

And one fine sun-splashed noon he lunged
  Over the stark deadline—and missed!
Swung for an instant and then plunged
  While the lone insane rivet hissed
Him all the way down from truss to truss
And dropped beside its Icarus!

The old strap-hanger thumbed his paper;
  Feet shuffled sidewalks; traffic roared. . . .
Icarus had performed his caper—
  Little New York minced by bored:
Leave the lads with broken backs,
Soiled feathers and some melted wax!

Joseph Auslander

LAVENDER LILIES

The lavender lilies in Garfield Park lay lazy in the morning sun.
A cool summer wind flicked at our eyebrows and the
  pansies fixed their yellow drops and circles for a day's
  show.
The statue of Lincoln, an ax in his hand, a bronze ax, was
  a chum of five bluejays crazy and calling, "Another
  lovely morning, another lovely morning."
And the headline of my newspaper said, "Thirty dead in
  race riots."
And Lincoln with the ax, and all the lavender lilies and
  the cool summer wind and the pansies, the living lips
  of bronze and leaves, the living tongues of jays, all
  they could say was,
"Another lovely morning, another lovely morning."

Carl Sandburg

THE KINGS ARE PASSING DEATHWARD

The Kings are passing deathward in the dark
  Of days that had been splendid where they went;
Their crowns are captive and their courts are stark
  Of purples that are ruinous, now, and rent.
For all that they have seen disastrous things:
  The shattered pomp, the split and shaken throne,
They cannot quite forget the way of Kings:
  Gravely they pass, majestic and alone.

51

With thunder on their brows, their faces set
   Toward the eternal night of restless shapes,
They walk in awful splendour, regal yet,
   Wearing their crimes like rich and kingly capes. . . .
Curse them or taunt, they will not hear or see;
The Kings are passing deathward: let them be.

David Morton

PART TWO

QUESTIONS AND SUGGESTIONS

A Book on Economics

Long is both a university professor and a poet. Which side of him comes uppermost here?

Has child labor been entirely outlawed yet?

What hint might you get from the poem concerning your reading of newspapers?

Seared

Here is a full-length picture of "a little boy at work" and the effect on him in later life. Is it more or less pathetic than it would have been if the man had been represented as still poor?

Boy with His Hair Cut Short

In this generation, what pictures other than those of sweat-shops lurk behind figures that we read?

The one picture given here is very detailed. How, then, does the poem set your imagination working?

After you have finished the collection, this poem and "Seared" are two that you should turn back to for contrasts in technique.

The Code

Is the chief impression of this poem humorous or serious? What is the point of the title? Why is it necessary to use one's imagination in dealing with other people? How does the sound of this poem suggest an altogether different type of person from the central figure of "Seared"?

The Pylons

Spender is an English poet. In America, what do we usually see carrying electric wires over hills and through the countryside? Do you (1) take them for granted, (2) think how ugly they look, or (3) think of the future they portend for country regions? Why would massive concrete pylons seem even more "tall with prophecy"? In England, what will happen to the "crumbling roads"? To the "hidden villages"? To the "emerald country"? What do you know about our TVA?

Wing Harbor

The poem tells you that the pilot was carrying mail. What might have made him want to turn his back on his duty?

"Then idly, *habit-chained,* his fingers found and shook the throttle." How many pictures can you see behind the italicized words?

Think over the last two lines of the poem.

Broadway

Has electricity benefited the modern city? What things about the Broadway evening crowds probably suggested the comparison to the poet? Why should he call them "far" when he is jostling elbows with them? Does anyone really get to know anyone else?

Legend

Since the days of Burns, dialect poetry has been considered legitimate. Yet when Weaver started to write "in American," critics complained that his work offended poetic taste. What do you think? Is the idea in this poem poetic? Are there any expressions that are primarily poetic? Are there any that detract from the poetic effect?

Does your imagination keep pace with that of the man in the poem?

Irradiations (III)

What three expressions in the poem suggest the ugliness of this scene? (What other features usually make rivers ugly near their mouths?) What details make the imaginary scene in the tropics vivid? Why are the two pictures put together?

Een Napoli

What two details here suggest life in a southern country? (By the way, Rome is on the same parallel of latitude as New York. What makes the difference in the Italian climate?) What does the Italian probably miss that is not mentioned here?

When your imagination works on mere suggestions (notice the contrast between this poem and "Irradiations"), the pictures it builds up are often inexact in detail. Does that make any difference in your pleasure?

Roses in the Subway

As the girl comes down the car, the poet notices first her face, second the roses and the way she is carrying them, and third the scent of the roses. What is the reason for that order? What is the similarity between this poem and "Een Napoli"? Give an instance where keen remembrance might be evoked by the sense of hearing; by the sense of touch.

The Riveter

Why did the crowds gather when the riveters came on the job? How high do you suppose the building had grown by the time the young man fell? Would you have noticed, as you saw him fall, that "the lone insane rivet hissed him all the way down"? Try to imagine what the following members of his "pavement audience" thought an hour after they had seen him fall: a small boy, a young girl, a foreman on the job, an old woman. What other jobs demand the risk of human lives? Try writing a poem yourself about one.

Lavender Lilies

Why was it necessary for the point of the poem that the statue should be of Lincoln rather than of some other great American? What makes powerful the contrast in the two pictures, one expressed and one left to the readers' imagination?

The orator said, "Why talk of beauty?" Is the beautification of public parks, for instance, a waste of money?

The Kings Are Passing Deathward

Three kinds of imagination enter into a full appreciation of this poem: ability to re-create pictures of the past, insight into feelings, and power to fancy something beyond human sight. With Morton's phrases to guide you, let your imagination ride along these three roads.

PART TWO

SUGGESTED SUPPLEMENTARY READING

Older Poems

Tam o' Shanter	Robert Burns
Simon Lee, the Old Huntsman	William Wordsworth
Song of the Shirt	Thomas Hood
Evelyn Hope	Robert Browning
Going Down Hill on a Bicycle	Henry Charles Beeching
Bill and Joe	Oliver Wendell Holmes
Jim Bludso of the Prairie Belle	John Hay
Crossing the Plains	Joaquin Miller
Uncle Gabe's White Folks	Thomas Nelson Page
"Extras"	Richard Burton

Newer Poems

Cassandra	Edwin Arlington Robinson
The Congo	Vachel Lindsay
Rear-Porches of an Apartment Building	Maxwell Bodenheim
The Monkey	Nancy Campbell
Caliban in the Coal Mines	Louis Untermeyer
A Young Boy	Jessica Nelson North
Distance	Babette Deutsch
Barbara	Ruth Comfort Mitchell
Color	W. W. Gibson

Part Three

Behold this dreamer cometh.

Genesis, XXXVIII, 19

FOREWORD

The poems in this section are about people who have dreamed—some of them as we do, some of them more than the rest of us. Because everyone dreams of different things, the words used to describe aspirations and memories must be especially well chosen if the readers are to understand and sympathize fully.

Strange as it may seem, words often give us better pictures or clearer ideas if the poet describes things not exactly, but indirectly through comparison or suggestion. So this seems a good place to consider figures of speech, and to examine words for their connotation; that is, their power to suggest more than they actually say.

The main tests for the excellence of figures of speech are vividness, appropriateness, and originality. The third is the really acid test. After reading even one thousand of the ten thousands of books in circulation, the ordinary individual feels that almost everything has been said before in almost every way; and all his life he is content to speak or write in *clichés,* as the French call expressions worn out by constant use. But the case is different with a poet who is worth his salt. (That figure of speech, by the way, is a cliché; how might the idea be better expressed?) He refuses to believe that he cannot find new and effective ways of saying things. Yet he tries to avoid going too far in his search for originality, for that might result in obscurity or inappropriateness. It should be interesting for you to notice how nearly right figures can be made.

THE SHEPHERD TO THE POET

Och, what's the good o' spinnin' words
    As fine as silken thread?
Will "golden gorse upon the hill"
    Be gold to buy ye bread?

An' while ye're list'nin' in the glen
    "To catch the thrush's lay,"
Your thatch is scattered be th' wind,
    Your sheep have gone astray.

Th' time ye're afther makin' rhymes
    O' "leppin' waves an' sea,"
Arrah! ye should be sellin' then
    Your lambs upon the quay.

Sure, 'tis God's ways is very quare,
    An' far beyont my ken,
How o' the selfsame clay he makes
    Poets an' useful men!

Agnes Kendrick Gray

THE BARREL-ORGAN

There's a barrel-organ caroling across a golden street
    In the City as the sun sinks low;
And the music's not immortal; but the world has made it
    sweet
    And fulfilled it with the sunset glow;

61

And it pulses through the pleasures of the City and the
   pain
   That surround the singing organ like a large eternal
      light;
And they've given it a glory and a part to play again
   In the Symphony that rules the day and night.

And now it's marching onward through the realms of old
      romance,
   And trolling out a fond familiar tune,
And now it's roaring cannon down to fight the King of
      France,
   And now it's prattling softly to the moon,
And all around the organ there's a sea without a shore
   Of human joys and wonders and regrets;
To remember and to recompense the music evermore
   For what the cold machinery forgets. . . .

Yes; as the music changes,
   Like a prismatic glass,
It takes the light and ranges
   Through all the moods that pass;
Dissects the common carnival
   Of passions and regrets,
And gives the world a glimpse of all
   The colours it forgets.

And there La Traviata sighs
   Another sadder song;
And there Il Trovatore cries
   A tale of deeper wrong;

And bolder knights to battle go
With sword and shield and lance,
Than ever here on earth below
Have whirled into—*a dance!*—

Go down to Kew in lilac-time, in lilac-time, in lilac-
time;
  Go down to Kew in lilac-time (it isn't far from London!)
And you shall wander hand in hand with love in summer's wonderland;
  Go down to Kew in lilac-time (it isn't far from London!)

The cherry-trees are seas of bloom and soft perfume and
sweet perfume,
  The cherry-trees are seas of bloom (and oh, so near to
London!)
And there they say, when dawn is high and all the world's
a blaze of sky
  The cuckoo, though he's very shy, will sing a song for
London.

The Dorian nightingale is rare and yet they say you'll
hear him there
  At Kew, at Kew in lilac-time (and oh, so near to
London!)
The linnet and the throstle, too, and after dark the long
halloo
  And golden-eyed *tu-whit, tu-whoo* of owls that ogle
London.

For Noah hardly knew a bird of any kind that isn't heard
  At Kew, at Kew in lilac-time (and oh, so near to
  London!)
And when the rose begins to pout and all the chestnut
  spires are out
  You'll hear the rest without a doubt, all chorusing for
  London:—

Come down to Kew in lilac-time, in lilac-time, in lilac-
  time;
  Come down to Kew in lilac-time (it isn't far from
  London!)
And you shall wander hand in hand with love in sum-
  mer's wonderland;
  Come down to Kew in lilac-time (it isn't far from
  London!)

And then the troubadour begins to thrill the golden street,
  In the City as the sun sinks low;
And in all the gaudy busses there are scores of weary feet
Marking time, sweet time, with a dull mechanic beat,
And a thousand hearts are plunging to a love they'll never
  meet,
Through the meadows of the sunset, through the poppies
  and the wheat,
In the land where the dead dreams go.

Verdi, Verdi, when you wrote Il Trovatore did you dream
  Of the City when the sun sinks low,
Of the organ and the monkey and the many-colored
  stream
On the Piccadilly pavement, of the myriad eyes that seem

To be litten for a moment with a wild Italian gleam
As *A che la morte* parodies the world's eternal theme
   And pulses with the sunset-glow?

There's a thief, perhaps, that listens with a face of frozen
     stone
   In the City as the sun sinks low;
There's a portly man of business with a balance of his
     own,
There's a clerk and there's a butcher of a soft reposeful
     tone.
And they're all of them returning to the heavens they
     have known:
They are crammed and jammed in busses and—they're
     each of them alone
   In the land where the dead dreams go.

There's a very modish woman and her smile is very bland
   In the City as the sun sinks low;
And her hansom jingles onward, but her little jeweled
     hand
Is clenched a little tighter and she cannot understand
What she wants or why she wanders to that undiscovered
     land,
For the parties there are not at all the sort of thing she
     planned,
   In the land where the dead dreams go.

There's a rowing man that listens and his heart is crying
     out
   In the City as the sun sinks low;

For the barge, the eight, the Isis, and the coach's whoop
and shout,
For the minute-gun, the counting and the long dishevelled
rout,
For the howl along the tow-path and a fate that's still in
doubt,
For a roughened oar to handle and a race to think about
In the land where the dead dreams go.

There's a laborer that listens to the voices of the dead
In the City as the sun sinks low;
And his hand begins to tremble and his face to smoulder
red
As he sees a loafer watching him and—there he turns his
head
And stares into the sunset where his April love is fled,
For he hears her softly singing and his lonely soul is led
Through the land where the dead dreams go.

There's an old and haggard demi-rep, it's ringing in her
ears,
In the City as the sun sinks low;
With the wild and empty sorrow of the love that blights
and sears,
Oh, and if she hurries onward, then be sure, be sure she
hears,
Hears and bears the bitter burden of the unforgotten
years,
And her laugh's a little harsher and her eyes are brimmed
with tears
For the land where the dead dreams go.

66

There's a barrel-organ caroling across a golden street
  In the City as the sun sinks low;
Though the music's only Verdi there's a world to make
    it sweet
Just as yonder yellow sunset where the earth and heaven
    meet
Mellows all the sooty City! Hark, a hundred thousand
    feet
Are marching on to glory through the poppies and the
    wheat
  In the land where the dead dreams go.

        So it's Jeremiah, Jeremiah,
          What have you to say
        When you meet the garland girls
          Tripping on their way?

        All around my gala hat
          I wear a wreath of roses
        (A long and lonely year it is
          I've waited for the May!)
        If anyone should ask you,
          The reason why I wear it is—
        My own love, my true love
          Is coming home to-day.

And it's buy a bunch of violets for the lady
  (*It's lilac-time in London; it's lilac-time in London!*)
Buy a bunch of violets for the lady
  While the sky burns blue above:

On the other side the street you'll find it shady
   (*It's lilac-time in London; it's lilac-time in London!*)
But buy a bunch of violets for the lady
   And tell her she's your own true love.

There's a barrel-organ caroling across a golden street
   In the City as the sun sinks glittering and slow;
And the music's not immortal; but the world has made it
   sweet
And enriched it with the harmonies that make a song
   complete
In the deeper heavens of music where the night and
   morning meet,
   As it dies into the sunset-glow;
And it pulses through the pleasures of the City and the
   pain
   That surround the singing organ like a large eternal
   light,
And they've given it a glory and a part to play again
   In the Symphony that rules the day and night.

     And there, as the music changes,
       The song runs round again.
     Once more it turns and ranges
       Through all its joy and pain,
     Dissects the common carnival
       Of passions and regrets;
     And the wheeling world remembers all
       The wheeling song forgets.

     Once more La Traviata sighs
       Another sadder song:

Once more Il Trovatore cries
A tale of deeper wrong;
Once more the knights to battle go
    With sword and shield and lance
Till once, once more, the shattered foe
Has whirled into—*a dance!*

Come down to Kew in lilac-time, in lilac-time, in lilac-
    time;
    Come down to Kew in lilac-time (it isn't far from
    London!)
And you shall wander hand in hand with love in sum-
    mer's wonderland;
    Come down to Kew in lilac-time (it isn't far from
    London!)   *Alfred Noyes*

PROVINCETOWN

All summer in the close-locked streets the crowd
Elbows its way past glittering shops to strains
Of noisy rag-time, men and girls, dark-skinned,—
From warmer foreign waters they have come
To our New England. Purring like sleek cats
The cushioned motors of the rich crawl through
While black-haired babies scurry to the curb:
Pedro, Maria, little Gabriel
Whose red bandana mothers selling fruit
Have this in common with the fresh white caps
Of those first immigrants—courage to leave
Familiar hearths and build new memories.

Blood of their blood who shaped these sloping roofs
And low arched doorways, laid the cobble stones
Not meant for motors,—you and I rejoice
When roof and spire sink deep into the night
And all the little streets reach out their arms
To be received into the salt-drenched dark.
Then Provincetown comes to her own again,
Draws round her like a cloak that shelters her
From too swift changes of the passing years
The dunes, the sea, the silent hilltop grounds
Where solemn groups of leaning headstones hold
Perpetual reunion of her dead.

At dusk we feel our way along the wharf
That juts into the harbor: anchored ships
With lifting prow and slowly rocking mast
Ink out their profiles; fishing dories scull
With muffled lamps that glimmer through the spray;
We hear the water plash among the piers
Rotted with moss, long after sunset stay
To watch the dim sky-changes ripple down
The length of quiet ocean to our feet
Till on the sea rim rising like a world
Bigger than ours, and laying bare the ships
In shadowy stillness, swells the yellow moon.

Between this blue intensity of sea
And rolling dunes of white-hot sand that burn
All day across a clean salt wilderness
On shores grown sacred as a place of prayer,
Shine bright invisible footsteps of a band
Of firm-lipped men and women who endured

Partings from kindred, hardship, famine, death,
And won for us three hundred years ago
A reverent proud freedom of the soul.

Marie Louise Hersey

DA YOUNGA 'MERICAN

I, Mysal', I feela strange
 Een dees countra. I can no
Mak' mysal' agen an' change
 Eento 'Merican, an' so
I am w'at you calla me,
 Justa "dumb ole Dago man."
Alla same my boy ees be
 Smarta younga 'Merican.
Twalv' year ole! but alla same
 He ees learna soocha lot
He can read an' write hees name—
 Smarta keed? I tal you w'at!

He no talk Italian;
 He says: "Dat's for Dagoes speak,
I am younga 'Merican,
 Dago langwadge mak' me seeck."
Eeef you gona tal heem, too,
 He ees "leetla Dago," my!
He ees gat so mad weeth you
 He gon' ponch you een da eye.
Mebbe so you gona mak'
 Fool weeth heem—an' mebbe not.

71

Queeck as flash he sass you back;
  Smarta keed? I tal you w'at!

He ees moocha 'shame' for be
  Meexa weeth Italian;
He ees moocha 'shame' of me—
  I am dumb ole Dago man.
Evra time w'en I go out
  Weetha heem I no can speak
To som'body. "Shut your mout',"
  He weell tal me pretta queeck,
"You weell geeve yoursal' away
  Talkin' Dago lika dat;
Try be 'Merican," he say—
  Smarta keed? I tal you w'at!

I am w'at you calla me,
  Justa "dumb ole Dago man:"
Alla same my boy ees be
  Smarta younga 'Merican.

T. A. Daly

MOTHER OF THE WORLD

I stopped in Oklahoma
Where a shack to a red hill clung,
And where nothing would grow except children,
Flaxen-haired, squat, brown babies!
Ten I counted, ragged and dirty—
The mother stood in the doorway.

Her hair hung cleated, sunburned to her head;
Her skin was rich and blistered like a man's
Hot from the ploughing; her body
Was ugly and strong, but her face
Lifted like a sunflower to the sun.
Shading her eyes with work-widened hands
She leaned against the doorway of the shack
Gazing not at me but through me,
Seeing not me—but the brown babes in the dirt.
Mother of the world she was
With dreams of making a new world in her eyes.

Visioned her children grown to youth
Beautiful and bold; saw her daughters
Graceful as maples silver-leafed, wind-blown,
With throats curved softly as catalpa blossoms
Flushed faintly with the tint of sunset gold.
Brides of strong men and bearing children,
Walking with their own brown babes at breast.
She saw her sons, stronger than their sire,
A new race to themselves, new men—
Slim saplings deepened into giant oaks!

Visioned the great muscled arms of her children
Ploughing, planting, making of common labor
Work divine; she pictured them
Templing the continents with their architecture,
Spanning the starry rivers with their bridges,
Rearing their coral columns to the sun!
All things perfect, planned by mortals,
Should know the imprint of her children's hands—

73

And, where they set their feet, new cities spring,
And where they stopped to plough, a new world grow!
Within the sun-glazed shack she stood,
Mother of the world, dreamer of dreams,
Beautiful to look upon, for in her eyes
Lay a dream of her brown children.

Enid Hayward

KANSAS BOY

This Kansas boy who never saw the sea
Walks through the young corn rippling at his knee
As sailors walk; and when the grain grows higher
Watches the dark waves leap with greener fire
Than ever oceans hold. He follows ships,
Tasting the bitter spray upon his lips,
For in his blood up-stirs the salty ghost
Of one who sailed a storm-bound English coast.
Across wide fields he hears the sea winds crying,
Shouts at the crows—and dreams of white gulls flying.

Ruth Lechlitner

IDEALISTS

Brother Tree:
Why do you reach and reach?
do you dream some day to touch the sky?
Brother Stream:
Why do you run and run?
do you dream some day to fill the sea?

Brother Bird:
Why do you sing and sing?
do you dream—

Young Man:
Why do you talk and talk and talk?

Alfred Kreymborg

SILENCE

I have known the silence of the stars and of the sea,
And the silence of the city when it pauses,
And the silence of a man and a maid,
And the silence for which music alone finds the word,
And the silence of the woods before the winds of spring
     begin,
And the silence of the sick
When their eyes roam about the room.
And I ask: For the depths
Of what use is language?
A beast of the fields moans a few times
When death takes its young.
And we are voiceless in the presence of realities—
We cannot speak.

A curious boy asks an old soldier
Sitting in front of the grocery store,
"How did you lose your leg?"
And the old soldier is struck with silence,
Or his mind flies away
Because he cannot concentrate it on Gettysburg.

It comes back jocosely
And he says, "A bear bit it off."
And the boy wonders, while the old soldier
Dumbly, feebly lives over
The flashes of guns, the thunder of cannon,
The shrieks of the slain,
And himself lying on the ground,
And the hospital surgeons, the knives,
And the long days in bed.
But if he could describe it all
He would be an artist.
But if he were an artist there would be deeper wounds
Which he could not describe.

There is the silence of a great hatred,
And the silence of a great love,
And the silence of a deep peace of mind,
And the silence of an embittered friendship.
There is the silence of a spiritual crisis,
Through which your soul, exquisitely tortured,
Comes with visions not to be uttered
Into a realm of higher life.
And the silence of the gods who understand each other
     without speech.
There is the silence of defeat.
There is the silence of those unjustly punished;
And the silence of the dying whose hand
Suddenly grips yours.
There is the silence between father and son,
When the father cannot explain his life,
Even though he be misunderstood for it.

There is the silence that comes between husband and wife.
There is the silence of those who have failed;
And the vast silence that covers
Broken nations and vanquished leaders.
There is the silence of Lincoln,
Thinking of the poverty of his youth.
And the silence of Napoleon
After Waterloo.
And the silence of Jeanne d'Arc
Saying amid the flames, "Blessed Jesus"—
Revealing in two words all sorrow, all hope.
And there is the silence of age,
Too full of wisdom for the tongue to utter it
In words intelligible to those who have not lived
The great range of life.

And there is the silence of the dead.
If we who are in life cannot speak
Of profound experiences,
Why do you marvel that the dead
Do not tell you of death?
Their silence shall be interpreted
As we approach them.

                              Edgar Lee Masters

SILHOUETTE

It quivered from the ground
And felt the air uphold its struggling wings,
The mounting aeroplane!

77

In the dim theater we watched its course
Upon the screen,
And saw it rise, until the villages
Were as toy houses ranged along a floor,
Till rivers and the roads seemed swirls of tape,
And only clouds were man-sized things and true!
So, up and up—across wide plains of sky
The sharp wings fared;
And we sat wondering, feet upon the earth,
But spirits lifted, racing with keen winds
That fly between the stars.
   And then—he stood—
The bulky man in front,
Drew on his coat, humped in thick folds,
His gloves,
Rounded his back and stooped to find his hat,
Stood square,
And blotted out the fluttering thing that held,
Singing within its engine's crowded space,
The spirit of a million million birds.

Hortense Flexner

CLEAN CURTAINS

New neighbors came to the corner house at Congress and
    Green streets.

The look of their clean white curtains was the same as the
    rim of a nun's bonnet.

78

One way was an oyster pail factory, one way they made
    candy, one way paper boxes, strawboard cartons.

The warehouse trucks shook the dust of the ways loose
    and the wheels whirled dust—there was dust of hoof
    and wagon wheel and rubber tire—dust of police and
    fire wagons—dust of the winds that circled at mid-
    nights and noon listening to no prayers.

"O mother, I know the heart of you," I sang passing the
    rim of a nun's bonnet—O white curtains—and people
    clean as the prayers of Jesus here in the faded ram-
    shackle at Congress and Green.

Dust and the thundering trucks won—the barrages of the
    street wheels and the lawless wind took their way—
    was it five weeks or six the little mother, the new
    neighbors, battled and then took away the white
    prayers in the windows?   *Carl Sandburg*

THE SAINT

Do you remember, Joan, (O vain to wonder
    if you remember how the evening star,
    a thousand times you drove the herd home under,
    admitted you to vision's Calendar,
            like any child
    by that tall friendship, and the quiet moon beguiled?)

Do you remember the Dom Rémy you knew,
    the plain and the small mountain-range of ricks,

79

the poplars at their goose-step, two by two,
the brown hen-church that folded her stone-chicks,
            your father's farm
so dear, so small it almost fitted in your arm?

Do you remember (even through the flame)
    after the long day's labour in the field
    how with the Angelus you heard your name
    mixed with the bells, and hid your face and kneeled
            when sweet and high
    a peasant heard "ecce ancilla Domini"?

"Behold the servant of the Lord—and France,"
    and in your hands, that never held a sword,
    the country staff was lifted like a lance
    in the hushed aisles of evening, to the Lord,
            and you were gone
    for ever, Joan, to put immortal iron on.

What was your sainthood, Joan? You did not guess
    when you restored his lilies to your king
    that you had found beyond the fleur-de-lys
    the lilies in an everlasting spring
            whose wind is blown
    across the centuries, and is fragrant, Joan.

You were not a proud saint. You went alone
    among the soldiers, and you understood
    how men are only frightened angels, Joan,
    and evil only unprotected good;
            you knew these things,
    and knew how pardonable are the hearts of kings.

And, being a woman, you lifted mankind up
  against the devil in their own despite,
  and when they feared, you drank the bitter cup
  for all your cowards as by woman's right,
            and, even when
  you burned, you did not blame them, knowing they
    were men.

Saint Joan, it may be all things human must
  be dull with earth, and with the darkness faint,
  but if it be so, then your mortal dust
  was purged with flame till you were all a saint,
            and when you prayed
  fire spoke to fire, and mixed in heaven, Maid.

Humbert Wolfe

GENERAL WILLIAM BOOTH
ENTERS INTO HEAVEN

(To be sung to the tune of *The Blood of the Lamb*
with indicated instrument)

I

[*Bass drum beaten loudly*]
Booth led boldly with his big bass drum—
(Are you washed in the blood of the Lamb?)
The Saints smiled gravely and they said: "He's come."
(Are you washed in the blood of the Lamb?)
Walking lepers followed, rank on rank,
Lurching bravoes from the ditches dank,

Drabs from the alleyways and drug fiends pale—
Minds still passion-ridden, soul-powers frail:—
Vermin-eaten saints with mouldy breath,
Unwashed legions with the ways of Death—
(Are you washed in the blood of the Lamb?)

[*Banjos*]
Every slum had sent its half-a-score
The round world over. (Booth had groaned for more.)
Every banner that the wide world flies
Bloomed with glory and transcendent dyes.
Big-voiced lasses made their banjos bang,
Tranced, fanatical, they shrieked and sang:—
"Are you washed in the blood of the Lamb?"
Hallelujah! It was queer to see
Bull-necked convicts with that land made free.
Loons with trumpets blowed a blare, blare, blare
On, on upward thro' the golden air!
(Are you washed in the blood of the Lamb?)

II

[*Bass drum slower and softer*]
Booth died blind and still by Faith he trod,
Eyes still dazzled by the ways of God.
Booth led boldly, and he looked the chief,
Eagle countenance in sharp relief,
Beard a-flying, air of high command
Unabated in that holy land.

[*Sweet flute music*]
Jesus came from out the court-house door,
Stretched his hands above the passing poor.

82

Booth saw not, but led his queer ones there
Round and round the mighty court-house square.
Yet in an instant all that blear review
Marched on spotless, clad in raiment new.
The lame were straightened, withered limbs uncurled
And blind eyes opened on a new, sweet world.

[*Bass drum louder*]
Drabs and vixens in a flash made whole!
Gone was the weasel-head, the snout, the jowl!
Sages and sibyls now, and athletes clean,
Rulers of empires, and of forests green!

[*Grand chorus of all instruments. Tambourines to the
    foreground.*]
The hosts were sandalled, and their wings were fire!
(Are you washed in the blood of the Lamb?)
But their noise played havoc with the angel-choir.
(Are you washed in the blood of the Lamb?)
O, shout Salvation! It was good to see
Kings and Princes by the Lamb set free.
The banjos rattled and the tambourines
Jing-jing-jingled in the hands of Queens.

[*Reverently sung, no instruments*]
And when Booth halted by the curb for prayer
He saw his Master thro' the flag-filled air.
Christ came gently with a robe and crown
For Booth the soldier, while the throng knelt down.
He saw King Jesus. They were face to face,
And he knelt a-weeping in that holy place.
Are you washed in the blood of the Lamb?

Vachel Lindsay

PART THREE

QUESTIONS AND SUGGESTIONS

The Shepherd to the Poet

What accusation that is always leveled against the dreamer lies in the shepherd's words? What determines the usefulness of dreamers to society?

"Golden" and "gold" are words very commonly used in poetry. To your mind, would there be any difference in meaning between "golden" and "gold" used as adjectives?

The comparison of writers to spinners is also frequent. Do you know whether spinning was hard work? whether it demanded skill? Do you know the original meaning of the word "poet"?

The Barrel-Organ

The people in this poem are all represented as dreaming of the past. Does that seem to you a natural result of listening to familiar music? What artistic effect does the poet gain by not mentioning dreams of the future?

Two kinds of comparison are used throughout. *Similes* compare things (things unlike in some respects but alike in at least one) by the words *like* or *as*. There are two very obvious ones in the first three stanzas; pick them out. *Metaphors* are not so apparent because no *like* or *as* is used and the comparison often lurks in one word: for example, "all the chestnut *spires* are out," in which the poet suggests to us the likeness in shape between the large, tapering blossom and a church spire. Try to find three others in the poem. One is especially good.

84

Provincetown

Provincetown, which lies at the tip of Cape Cod, was one of the first Puritan settlements. The recent settlers are mostly Portuguese. What qualities of character have immigrants possessed?

Tell the objects compared and the point of comparison in the following expressions: "Purring like sleek cats / The cushioned motors of the rich crawl through"; "anchored ships . . . , Ink out their profiles."

An expression which compares an inanimate object or some lower form of life to a human being is called *personification*. Find two such in the second verse-paragraph. Are they effective?

Da Younga 'Merican

Twelve is a thoughtless age. What does the boy fail to realize about his father? Why is the father still proud of him?

Two words that the immigrant has picked up are rich in connotations—"dumb" and "smart." How did "dumb" come to be used in its present slang sense? Is "smart" ever an uncomplimentary word? What pictures do the words bring to you through personal remembrance or association?

Mother of the World

In your dreams of the future for yourself or for anyone else, do you picture only pleasant things? Would a mother who had known great hardship be more or less apt to dream of her children's overcoming hardships?

There is a new figure here in the lines "All things perfect, planned by mortals / Should know the imprint of her children's hands." This is deliberate exaggeration for effect; it is called *hyperbole*. Are there other instances of it in the poem?

Kansas Boy

What is the reason the poet gives for the nature of the boy's dreams? Have you ever tried to trace any of your day-dreams to some possible source?

Pick out one metaphor and one personification. Are they vivid?

"Salty ghost" illustrates a fifth figure. You have heard sailors called "salts," haven't you? Or a certain type of dinner a "blueplate"? Or the girl companion of the evening a "date"? All these terms are *metonomy* (often spelled *metonymy*)—a figure in which a thing is represented by the name of something else closely associated with it. In "The Barrel-Organ" there is another example in the line, "And then the troubadour begins to thrill the golden street." Try to think of others.

Idealists

Explain how the personifications help the central idea.

Silence

Can you appreciate both talk and silence as evidence of people's dreams?

Because this poem catalogues many deep human experiences, the words it uses are full of connotations. A very obvious example is "Waterloo." Even when it is used without any mention of Napoleon, it carries the sense of defeat.

Silhouette

"Feet upon the earth,
But spirits lifted"

Do moving pictures make people dream as much as other forms of art do? Might your dream be broken in an art gallery, or at a concert?

Do you like the similes used here? The hyperbole?

Clean Curtains

This poem is an outstanding example of the use of symbolism. What do the white curtains represent? What commentary on city life is left in your mind?

The metaphors and similes, striking in themselves, are made still more effective by subtle forms of repetition. Ask your teacher to read the poem aloud, and listen carefully.

The Saint

"Hushed," "fragrant," "purged"—each of these words should suggest to you several different things. Try pooling the pictures in class to see how varied connotations may be.

To address an absent person as present, or a dead person as living, is to use the figure called *apostrophe*. Many poets do it occasionally, but few carry it through a whole poem.

Examine the figures in the following words: "mountain-range of ricks," "brown hen-church," "hushed aisles of evening," "immortal iron," "restored his lilies," "drank the bitter cup." Are the expressions appropriate? What picture of Joan herself do you see against the background of each?

General William Booth Enters into Heaven

Vachel Lindsay had very striking methods of reciting his poetry. Sometimes he actually sang it, as is indicated here. Most of the time he chanted the lines, stressing the accented syllables strongly, and pausing definitely between the feet. He used the full range and power of his marvelous voice, with effects shading from *fortissimo* to *pianissimo*. Fortunately he made a few records, three of which (*Congo, Kansas,* and *John R. Sullivan*) are commercially distributed by Walter C. Garwick, Sound Recording Instruments, Rye, New York, at $1.50 each. Teachers who are members of the National Council of Teachers of English may order these from him through the N.C.T.E. for $1.00 each.

Are the first four lines of the second stanza hyperbole? What is the metaphor that runs throughout?

How did Booth's dream differ from any of the others portrayed in this group?

PART THREE

SUGGESTED SUPPLEMENTARY READING

Older Poems

The Soldier's Dream	Thomas Campbell
A Dream of the Unknown	Percy Bysshe Shelley
The Realm of Fancy	John Keats
Ulysses	Alfred Tennyson
Rabbi Ben Ezra	Robert Browning
Dream-Pedlary	Thomas Lovell Beddoes
"Each life converges to some centre"	Emily Dickinson
My Lost Youth	Henry Wadsworth Longfellow
Drifting	Thomas Buchanan Read
Who Knows?	Nora Perry

Newer Poems

Jim	John Russell McCarthy
As I Grew Older	Langston Hughes
Portrait of a Boy	Stephen Vincent Benét
Music Comes	John Freeman
The Chinese Nightingale	Vachel Lindsay
The Bridge-Builders	Evelyn P. Simms
Birth	Lucia Trent

Part Four

Nature never did betray
The heart that loved her.

Wordsworth

FOREWORD

In this age of scientific accuracy that extends even to the details of a French queen's headdress in a historical motion picture, we find it hard to realize that only two hundred years ago a poet was highly praised for a poem "describing" a certain famous English forest in terms that would have applied just as well to any other forest on the island. For the modern feeling that a poet should "keep his eye on the object," that is, observe accurately and use exact words, we have to thank Burns and Wordsworth. They described individual scenes and people rather than types, and did not attempt to "prettify."

Modern descriptive poems of nature, like those presented in this section, show poets following the same general rules for description that you are given in your composition courses: (1) select the details that seem most important; (2) bring out the distinguishing features of each object described; (3) follow a logical sequence in time or place; (4) recreate the general mood produced by the scene. Comparisons, often made through figures of speech, help very much to accomplish the last result. But for the first three, the important thing is accurate observation, in which all five senses aid. Read carefully, and judge whether poets' senses are keener than yours and more truly recorded.

BIRCHES

When I see birches bend to left and right
Across the lines of straighter darker trees,
I like to think some boy's been swinging them.
But swinging doesn't bend them down to stay.
Ice-storms do that. Often you must have seen them
Loaded with ice a sunny winter morning
After a rain. They click upon themselves
As the breeze rises, and turn many-colored
As the stir cracks and crazes their enamel.
Soon the sun's warmth makes them shed crystal shells
Shattering and avalanching on the snow-crust—
Such heaps of broken glass to sweep away
You'd think the inner dome of heaven had fallen.
They are dragged to the withered bracken by the load,
And they seem not to break; though once they are bowed
So low for long, they never right themselves:
You may see their trunks arching in the woods
Years afterwards, trailing their leaves on the ground
Like girls on hands and knees that throw their hair
Before them over their heads to dry in the sun.
But I was going to say when Truth broke in
With all her matter-of-fact about the ice-storm
(Now am I free to be poetical?)
I should prefer to have some boy bend them
As he went out and in to fetch the cows—
Some boy too far from town to learn baseball,
Whose only play was what he found himself,
Summer or winter, and could play alone.
One by one he subdued his father's trees
By riding them down over and over again

Until he took the stiffness out of them,
And not one but hung limp, not one was left
For him to conquer. He learned all there was
To learn about not launching out too soon
And so not carrying the tree away
Clear to the ground. He always kept his poise
To the top branches, climbing carefully
With the same pains you use to fill a cup
Up to the brim, and even above the brim.
Then he flung outward, feet first, with a swish,
Kicking his way down through the air to the ground.
So was I once myself a swinger of birches.
And so I dream of going back to be.
It's when I'm weary of considerations,
And life is too much like a pathless wood
Where your face burns and tickles with the cobwebs
Broken across it, and one eye is weeping
From a twig's having lashed across it open.
I'd like to get away from earth awhile
And then come back to it and begin over.
May no fate willfully misunderstand me
And half grant what I wish and snatch me away
Not to return. Earth's the right place for love:
I don't know where it's likely to go better.
I'd like to go by climbing a birch tree,
And climb black branches up a snow-white trunk
Toward heaven, till the tree could bear no more,
But dipped its top and set me down again.
That would be good both going and coming back.
One could do worse than be a swinger of birches.

Robert Frost

HILLS RUDDY WITH SUMACH

Of New England,
Men who have never been there
Say that it is hard, cold, and iron;
Cold as the Pilgrim forefathers,
Hard as their courage,
Iron as the discipline of their hearts.

Of Massachusetts,
Men who have never seen it
Say that it is dour, stern, and rigid;
Dour as the conscience of a Puritan,
Rigid as the mind of a Puritan,
Stern as his uncompromising will.

They have never, then, gone from Plymouth to Scituate
    in the fragile and tender springtime
When the first stars of the wildflowers—
Mayflowers (the ship's name was *Mayflower*)
Violets, anemones—
Are scattered in the young grass.

They can never have tramped, then, blowing Cape Cod
    dunes in late August,
When the wind, always with a tang of salt, ruffles the
    white daisies,
When the wind, always from the sea, ruffles the Queen
    Anne's lace and the yarrow,
Swirls like waves the wild indigo, the yellow sweet-clover,
Ripples through the steeplebush, mustard, ragged robin,
Blowing always from the sea.

They can never have breathed deeply the sharp, harshly
　　fine air of Duxbury salt marshes in the autumn
(Behind, hills are yellow with goldenrod, purple with
　　asters;
Behind, hills are ruddy with sumach, red with choke-
　　cherry,
And the grim Rock out of sight around the corner)
When the herring gulls dip and plunge, shrieking dis-
　　cordantly as cymbals,
When the great herons rise slowly and leisurely out of
　　the green bending grasses,
And the brant pause, turning south.

Thomas Caldecot Chubb

FOUR LITTLE FOXES

Speak gently, Spring, and make no sudden sound;
For in my windy valley, yesterday I found
New-born foxes squirming on the ground—
　　　　Speak gently.

Walk softly, March, forbear the bitter blow;
Her feet within a trap, her blood upon the snow,
The four little foxes saw their mother go—
　　　　Walk softly.

Go lightly, Spring, oh, give them no alarm;
When I covered them with boughs to shelter them from
　　harm,
The thin blue foxes suckled at my arm—
　　　　Go lightly.

Step softly, March, with your rampant hurricane;
Nuzzling one another, and whimpering with pain,
The new little foxes are shivering in the rain—
        Step softly.   *Lew Sarett*

HAYMAKING

After night's thunder far away had rolled,
The fiery day had a kernel sweet of cold,
And in the perfect blue the clouds uncurled,
Like the first gods before they made the world
And misery, swimming the stormless sea
In beauty and in divine gaiety.
The smooth white empty road was lightly strewn
With leaves—the holly's Autumn falls in June—
And fir cones standing stiff up in the heat.
The mill-foot water tumbled white and lit
With tossing crystals, happier than any crowd
Of children pouring out of school aloud.
And in the little thickets where a sleeper
Forever might lie lost, the nettle-creeper
And garden warbler sang unceasingly;
While over them shrill shrieked in his fierce glee
The swift with wings and tail as sharp and narrow
As if the bow had flown off with the arrow.
Only the scent of woodbine and hay new-mown
Traveled the road. In the field sloping down,
Park-like, to where its willows showed the brook,
Haymakers rested. The tosser lay forsook
Out in the sun; and the long wagon stood
Without its team; it seemed it never would

Move from the shadow of that single yew.
The team, as still, until their task was due,
Beside the laborers enjoyed the shade
That three squat oaks mid-field together made
Upon a circle of grass and weed uncut,
And on the hollow, once a chalk-pit, but
Now brimmed with nut and elder-flower so clean.
The men leaned on their rakes, about to begin,
But still. And all were silent. All was old,
This morning time, with a great age untold,
Older than Clare and Cobbett, Morland and Crome,
Than, at the field's far edge, the farmer's home,
A white house crouched at the foot of a great tree.
Under the heavens that know not what years be
The men, the beasts, the trees, the implements
Uttered even what they will in times far hence—
All of us gone out of the reach of change—
Immortal in a picture of an old grange.

Edward Thomas

IRRADIATIONS

x

The trees, like great jade elephants,
Chained, stamp and shake 'neath the gadflies of the
    breeze;
The trees lunge and plunge, unruly elephants:
The clouds are their crimson howdah-canopies,
The sunlight glints like the golden robe of a Shah.
Would I were tossed on the wrinkled backs of those trees.

John Gould Fletcher

98

TO THE THAWING WIND

Come with rain, O loud Southwester!
Bring the singer, bring the nester;
Give the buried flower a dream;
Make the settled snow-bank steam;
Find the brown beneath the white;
But whatever you do to-night,
Bathe my window, make it flow,
Melt it as the ices go;
Melt the glass and leave the sticks
Like a hermit's crucifix;
Burst into my narrow stall;
Swing the picture on the wall;
Run the rattling pages o'er;
Scatter poems on the floor;
Turn the poet out of door.

Robert Frost

BIRDS

The fierce musical cries of a couple of sparrowhawks
    hunting on the headland,
Hovering and darting, their heads northwestward,
Prick like silver arrows shot through a curtain the noise
    of the ocean
Trampling its granite; their red backs gleam
Under my window around the stone corners; nothing
    gracefuller, nothing

Nimbler in the wind. Westward the wave-gleaners,
The old gray sea-going gulls are gathered together, the
    northwest wind wakening
Their wings to the wild spirals of the wind-dance.
Fresh as the air, salt as the foam, play birds in the bright
    wind, fly falcons
Forgetting the oak and the pinewood, come gulls
From the Carmel sands and the sands at the river-mouth,
    from Lobos and out of the limitless
Power of the mass of the sea, for a poem
Needs multitude, multitudes of thoughts, all fierce, all
    flesh-eaters, musically clamorous
Bright hawks that hover and dart headlong, and ungainly
Gray hungers fledged with desire of transgression, salt
    slimed beaks, from the sharp
Rock-shores of the world and the secret waters.

Robinson Jeffers

HIGH-TIDE

I edged back against the night.
The sea growled assault on the wave-bitten shore,
And the breakers,
Like young and impatient hounds,
Sprang, with rough joy, on the shrinking sand,
Sprang—but were drawn back slowly,
With a long, relentless pull,
Whimpering, into the dark.

Then I saw who held them captive;
And I saw how they were bound
With a broad and quivering leash of light,
Held by the moon,
As, calm and unsmiling,
She walked the deep fields of the sky.

Jean Starr Untermeyer

CARDIGAN BAY

Clean, green, windy billows notching out the sky,
Grey clouds tattered into rags, sea-winds blowing high,
And the ships under topsails, beating, thrashing by,
    And the mewing of the herring gulls.

Dancing, flashing green seas shaking white locks,
Boiling in blind eddies over hidden rocks,
And the wind in the rigging, the creaking of the blocks,
    And the straining of the timber hulls.

Delicate cool sea-weeds, green and amber-brown,
Beds where shaken sunlight slowly filters down
On many a drowned seventy-four, and many a sunken
    town,
    And the whitening of the dead men's skulls.

John Masefield

WILD STRAWBERRIES

The wild red strawberries are found
Inside the grass near the hot ground
In fields where clover, meadow rue
And shining daisies dry their dew.
Dip down between warm stem and stem
With your cool hand and look for them,
They hang on little stunted stems
In glowing clusters bright as gems
In secret nooks where warmness slips
Over your hand and finger tips,
They taste of dew and night, and warm
Sweet flowers scented by the sun.

Mary Britton Miller

THE GARDEN BY MOONLIGHT

A black cat among roses,
Phlox, lilac-misted under a first-quarter moon,
The sweet smells of heliotrope and night-scented stock.
The garden is very still,
It is dazed with moonlight,
Contented with perfume,
Dreaming the opium dreams of its folded poppies.
Firefly lights open and vanish
High as the tip buds of the golden glow,
Low as the sweet alyssum flowers at my feet.
Moon-shimmer on leaves and trellises,
Moon-spikes shafting through the snow-ball bush.

Only the little faces of the ladies' delight are alert and
    staring,
Only the cat, padding between the roses,
Shakes a branch and breaks the chequered pattern
As water is broken by the falling of a leaf.
Then you come.
And you are quiet like the garden,
And white like the alyssum flowers,
And beautiful as the silent sparks of the fireflies.
Ah, Beloved, do you see those orange lilies?
They knew my mother,
But who belonging to me will they know
When I am gone?

                  Amy Lowell

HIGHMOUNT

  Hills, you have answered the craving
     That spurred me to come;
  You have opened your deep blue bosom
     And taken me home.

The sea had filled me with the stress
Of its own restlessness;
My voice was in that angry roll
Of passion beating upon the world.
The ground beneath me shifted; I was swirled
In an implacable flood that howled to see
Its breakers rising in me,
A torrent rushing through my soul.

And tearing things free
I could not control.
A monstrous impatience, a stubborn and vain
Repetition of madness and longing, of question and pain,
Driving me up to the brow of this hill—
Calling and questioning still.

And you—you smile
In ordered calm;
You wrap yourself in cloudy contemplation while
The winds go shouting their heroic psalm,
The streams press lovingly about your feet
And trees, like birds escaping from the heat,
Sit in great flocks and fold their broad green wings. . . .
A cow bell rings
Like a sound blurred by sleep,
Giving the silence a rhythm
That makes it twice as deep. . . .
Somewhere a farm-hand sings. . . .

And here you stand
Breasting the elemental sea,
And put forth an invisible hand
To comfort me.
Rooted in quiet confidence, you rise
Above the frantic and assailing years;
Your silent faith is louder than the cries;
The shattering fears
Break and subside when they encounter you.
You know their doubts, the desperate questions—
And the answers too.

Hills, you are strong; and my burdens
  Are scattered like foam.
You have opened your deep, blue bosom
  And taken me home.

Louis Untermeyer

COAST CATHEDRAL

Alone on the cliff. Below me fathoms deep
Come echoes tumbling out of ocean caves
Whose overtones arouse me like the leap
Of *Sursum Corda* high in Gothic naves.

Alone, and yet the scent of bayberry leaves,
Mingled with briny savor, floods the air
With incense which my weariness receives
Like hyssop drifting from an altar stair.

How can I feel alone when great clouds run
Out of the north and poise above the sea,
Flanking the bright rose window of the sun
With blue-white panels of immensity?

A gliding gull descending from the sky,
An unexpected porpoise puffing near,
A gray-black harbor seal, nose lifted high,
Saint Francis might call brothers were he here.

And he would know that symbols others find
In vast cathedrals flowering out of Rome
To minister to something more than mind,
Emerge where dark cliffs kneel in ocean foam.

Wilbert Snow

THE UNSEEN

Who goes, touching the elm boughs as he goes,
These early mornings of the early frost?
Who moves amid the tall corn's myriad rows,
Whispering through their ranks, "Your war is lost"?
Who takes the tattered garland of the leaves
From the bent shoulders of an aged oak?
Now there is weeping in the hills. Who grieves?
Last night, among the rotted leaves, who spoke?

George O'Neil

REPROOF TO DEATH

Death, you are too small a thing to-day,
This April interval when the very wind
Grows up the sky and has a heart and body
Instinct with spring, for me to think you are
That proud and arrogant being men have feared,
That pestilential presence sung in grave
Timorous language by the living, that
Solemn power of sonorous speech
That with the ancient logic of the earth
Can argue men from life.
                              Against the beating
Wings of returning birds you are a small
Creature found rustling in the last year's leaves,
Cold with the wind, warmed in the hands, and held
Against the cheek until the soft breast tremble
And you are pitied and let down to crouch

Behind a stone.
                    Against the importunate
Sun that defies the land pull, driving the wild
Grape to implore the shadow-purpled sky
With lean life-twisted arms, that gold relentless
Globe that strides the universe and draws
Earth spinning after it, that energy
That mates the eagle on the mountain peak,
The elk beneath the pine, you seem, frail Death,
No stronger than this river water I
Silverly shatter with my foot, than this
Old autumn leaf the yelping hounds of wind
Harry across the heavens.
                    On this day
When life bursts through the world, and soil and flesh
Reel to contain it; when the sun tears water
Out of the sea and hurls it to the clouds—
You are, Death, on this eager day when crows
Clatter above the seeded field at dawn
Their rain-presaging cries; when the sun-seeking
Sparrow-hawks, maddened with mating, mount and soar
Beyond the sunlight; when the cedar roots,
Groping for rain, split rock—on this day you are
Deeply defied with living.
                    You are the only
Mortal thing; this morning strong with life
Brings death to you, Death.
                    Now in this world through which
The pulse of spring moves like a living blood
Down through the frost-split arteries of earth,
Up in the slender body of the wind,
Hollowly veined with the vireo's flight, to urge

Its various beat through dog-tooth violet,
Quail in the valley, great horse ploughing the hill,
There is only life. Death, you were the shadow
Cast by the living of the earth that now
Are utterly involved in the vast light
Of spring, that will be shadowless until
Life and that light dissolve.

                Not even with twilight
Will you return, for then the multitudes
Of living forms, then every hungry thing
To mock you, Death, will take life from the long
Hands of moonlight fumbling in the hills.

Paul Engle

PART FOUR

QUESTIONS AND SUGGESTIONS

Birches

In writing about white birches, Frost might have picked out many other details, for they are very picturesque trees. Why do you think he chose the occasional slanting shape as material for a poem?

Which picture is more vivid to you—that of the slender tree in an ice-storm, or that of the boy swinging the tree? Why?

Hills Ruddy with Sumach

Why did the poet not describe winter in New England? Why did he put in so much color? To what other senses besides sight does the poem appeal?

Three expressions, "ruffles," "stirs like waves," "ripples," are used to express the motion of the salty wind through various types of flowers. Tell why each one is exact.

Four Little Foxes

One device very common in poetry about nature is not usually classed with figures of speech, although it always implies personification. The "pathetic fallacy," as it is called, is the attributing of human emotions to inanimate things. What emotion is nature here represented as capable of feeling? Is it far from the truth?

Some pathetic fallacies seem more likely than others; but whenever a poet uses the device, he should produce in his readers the mood which Coleridge termed "a willing suspension of disbelief." What details has Sarett picked out that make us eager to believe that nature may be kind to the baby foxes?

Haymaking

Four pictures precede the main one of an English haymaking scene. What does each one contribute to the total effect? Notice that the picture of the haymakers is introduced by the scent of the hay. Why? Does the scene make you feel hot or cool, tired or rested?

"All of us gone out of the reach of change." Will the essential features of farming always be the same?

Irradiations (X)

Does "great jade elephants" suggest trees alike or different in shape and size from "three squat oaks"? What is the important thing about the trees in this poem? What words give the sense of it? Does the odd comparison help, or does it distract your attention?

Mr. Fletcher was one of six well-known poets who in 1912 classed themselves as "Imagists." The first article of their poetic creed was, "To use the language of common speech, but to employ always the *exact* word, not the nearly exact, nor the merely decorative word."

To the Thawing Wind

Is there more or less feeling of motion here than in the previous poem? What sounds does it make you hear?

Birds

Robinson Jeffers and his two sons helped to build a house made all of stones from the rocky coast, on a little peninsula just outside the town of Carmel, California. Apart from the proper names, does anything in the poem show that the ocean is the Pacific? What phrases keep its salt freshness in your nostrils?

What details distinguish the hawks from the gulls? Do you usually think of birds as "fierce"?

High-Tide

"The sea growled assault on the wave-bitten shore"
"The noise of the ocean / Trampling its granite"

What different types of shore line do these words suggest? Motion seems greater when it is contrasted with slower motion, or with something static. What is the contrast here? Is "calm and unsmiling" a pathetic fallacy?

Cardigan Bay

Written before the days when moving pictures were common, this poem nevertheless employs the method of a movie camera. How?

Does anything in the first two stanzas prepare us for the last two lines?

Are the words "notching out" and "shaken" exact?

Wild Strawberries

This is a static picture, given from one point of view. Have you had any like it so far?

Through what senses could a blind man appreciate nearly all the beauty of this experience?

The Garden by Moonlight

Why are the first three lines the most important of the sixteen preceding the words, "Then you come"? What do the other thirteen add? What does the introduction of the black cat contribute to the picture?

Highmount

What other poems have you had in this group where the descriptive element is bound up with the poets' personal feelings?

How long ago did someone say, in his own tongue, "I will lift up mine eyes unto the hills, from whence cometh my help"? Why have mountains often made men feel calm and strong?

Coast Cathedral

"De gustibus non est disputandum." Might another man who, like Wilbert Snow, was born in a seacoast town find calmness and strength near the ocean? What additional feeling is expressed here? Why is the mention of St. Francis of Assisi appropriate?

Try to find some picture of a great cathedral that will illustrate a Gothic nave, an altar stair, and a rose window.

The Unseen

What mood is the poet trying to produce in his readers?

In a poem as short as this, details must be selected with great care. What seems to have been the purpose in selecting and arranging these?

Reproof to Death

Paul Engle was under twenty when he wrote this. What marks it as the work of a young man?

What is common to all the details of the spring landscape that he mentions? What attribute of death does it seem to refute?

Can you, in a mood of jubilation, make yourself believe the impossible?

PART FOUR

SUGGESTED SUPPLEMENTARY READING

Older Poems

Spring	Thomas Nashe
Winter	William Shakespeare
"A wet sheet and a flowing sea" .	Allan Cunningham
To a Mountain Daisy	Robert Burns
Written in Early Spring . .	William Wordsworth
To Autumn	John Keats
The Deep	J. G. C. Brainard
Mist	Henry David Thoreau
"A narrow fellow in the grass" .	Emily Dickinson
"I'll tell you how the sun rose" .	Emily Dickinson
The Stars	Mary Mapes Dodge

Newer Poems

Velvet Shoes	Elinor Wylie
Heat	"H. D."
Clouds	Edward Shanks
Hurt Hawks	Robinson Jeffers
First Concerns . . .	Abbie Huston Evans
The Making of Birds . .	Katharine Tynan
"The evening darkens over" .	Robert Bridges
Loveliest of Trees . . .	A. E. Housman
Mending Wall	Robert Frost

Part Five

For what can war but endless war still breed?

Milton

FOREWORD

The oldest poems in any language were usually stories of exploits by racial heroes, told from what is called the *objective* point of view; that is, as if the poet were standing somewhere outside the circle of action, watching what happened so intently that he forgot all about himself. As time went on, however, poets became so interested in their own joys, sorrows, and philosophies of life that they desired to express themselves *subjectively*. Using the circle figure again, we might say that this time they themselves were in the middle of the circle.

For hundreds of years these two basic methods of presentation have been used in poetry, both so well that it is hard to say which is the more effective. You have had clear examples of each in the poems so far. In the following ones on the subject of war, the personal element can be seen in the ascendant.

Within both methods the authors have different ways of conveying emotions and ideas. Sometimes they say exactly what they mean; again, they use *irony,* a veil of words that deceives no one as to the meaning underneath. Often they "unpack their hearts with words," sparing no detail; in contrast, they may give only the barest outline of a picture or hint of a feeling, so that our imaginations can fill in the rest. A very common choice that they must make is between stating an idea in general terms or showing how it applies to some particular situation.

You might think of all these ways of presentation as lights of different colors played over objects or persons on a stage, in varying degrees of brilliancy or softness, sharpness or diffuseness. How different an impression the audience would get each time!

DULCE ET DECORUM EST

Bent double, like old beggars under sacks,
Knock-kneed, coughing like hags, we cursed through
     sludge,
Till on the haunting flares we turned our backs,
And towards our distant rest began to trudge.
Men marched asleep. Many had lost their boots,
But limped on, blood-shod. All went lame, all blind;
Drunk with fatigue; deaf even to the hoots
Of gas-shells dropping softly behind.

Gas! GAS! Quick, boys!—An ecstasy of fumbling
Fitting the clumsy helmets just in time,
But someone still was yelling out and stumbling
And flound'ring like a man in fire or lime—
Dim through the misty panes and thick green light,
As under a green sea, I saw him drowning.

In all my dreams before my helpless sight
He plunges at me, guttering, choking, drowning.

If in some smothering dreams, you too could pace
Behind the wagon that we flung him in,
And watch the white eyes writhing in his face,
His hanging face, like a devil's sick of sin,
If you could hear, at every jolt, the blood
Come gargling from the froth-corrupted lungs
Bitten as the cud
Of vile, incurable sores on innocent tongues,—

My friend, you would not tell with such high zest
To children ardent for some desperate glory,
The old LIE: *Dulce et decorum est
Pro patria mori!*

Wilfred Owen

COUNTER-ATTACK

We'd gained our first objective hours before
While dawn broke like a face with blinking eyes,
Pallid, unshaven and thirsty, blind with smoke,
Things seemed all right at first. We held their line,
With bombers posted, Lewis guns well placed,
And clink of shovels deepening the shallow trench.

The place was rotten with dead; green clumsy legs
High-booted, sprawled and grovelled along the saps;
And trunks, face downward, in the sucking mud,
Wallowed like trodden sand-bags loosely filled;
And naked sodden buttocks, mats of hair,
Bulged, clotted heads slept in the plastering slime.
And then the rain began,—the jolly old rain!

A yawning soldier knelt against the bank,
Staring across the morning blear with fog;
He wondered when the Allemands would get busy;
And then, of course, they started with five-nines
Traversing, sure as fate, and never a dud.
Mute in the clamor of shells he watched them burst
Spouting dark earth and wire gusts from hell,

While posturing giants dissolved in drifts of smoke.
He crouched and flinched, dizzy with galloping fear,
Sick for escape,—loathing the strangled horror
And butchered, frantic gestures of the dead.

An officer came blundering down the trench:
"Stand-to and man the fire-step!"   On he went . . .
Gasping and bawling.   "Fire-step . . . counter-attack!"
    Then the haze liftèd.   Bombing on the right
    Down the old sap: machine-guns on the left;
    And stumbling figures looming out in front.
    "O Christ, they're coming at us!"   Bullets spat,

And he remembered his rifle . . . rapid fire . . .
And started blazing wildly . . . then a bang
Crumpled and spun him sideways, knocked him out
To grunt and wriggle: none heeded him; he choked
And fought the flapping veils of smothering gloom,
Lost in a blurred confusion of yells and groans . . .
Down, and down, and down, he sank and drowned,
Bleeding to death.   The counter-attack had failed.

Siegfried Sassoon

REFUGEES

(Belgium—1914)

"Mother, the poplars cross the moon;
   The road runs on, so white and far
We shall not reach the city soon:
   Oh, tell me where we are!"

"Have patience, patience, little son,
    And we shall find the way again:
(God show me the untraveled one!
    God give me rest from men!)"

"Mother, you did not tell me why
    You hurried so to come away.
I saw big soldiers riding by;
    I should have liked to stay."

"Hush, little man, and I will sing
    Just like a soldier, if I can—
They have a song for everything.
    Listen, my little man!

"This is the soldiers' marching song:
    We'll play this is the village street—"
"Yes, but this road is very long,
    And stones have hurt my feet."

"Nay, little pilgrim, up with you!
    And yonder field shall be the town.
I'll show you how the soldiers do
    Who travel up and down.

"They march and sing and march again,
    Not minding all the stones and dust:
They go (God grant me rest from men!)
    Forward because they must."

"Mother, I want to go to sleep."
    "No, darling! Here is bread to eat!
(O God, if thou couldst let me weep,
    Or heal my broken feet!)"

                    Grace Hazard Conkling

AN OPEN BOAT

O what is that whimpering there in the darkness?
   "Let him lie in my arms. He is breathing, I know.
Look. I'll wrap all my hair round his neck."—
     "The sea's rising,
The boat must be lightened. He's dead. He must go."

See—quick—by that flash, where the bitter foam tosses,
   The cloud of white faces, in the black open boat,
And the wild pleading woman that clasps her dead lover
   And wraps her loose hair round his breast and his
     throat.

"Come, lady, he's dead." "No, I feel his heart beating.
   He's living, I know. But he's numbed with the cold.
See, I'm wrapping my hair all around him to warm
     him."—
   "No. We can't keep the dead, dear. Come, loosen
     your hold.

"Come. Loosen your fingers."—"O God, let me keep
     him!"
   O, hide it, black night! Let the winds have their way!
For there are no voices or ghosts from that darkness,
   To fret the bare seas at the breaking of day.

                              Alfred Noyes

NOON

(1 from "Battle")

It is midday: the deep trench glares . . .
A buzz and blaze of flies. . . .
The hot wind puffs the giddy airs. . . .
The great sun rakes the skies.

No sound in all the stagnant trench
Where forty standing men
Endure the sweat and grit and stench,
Like cattle in a pen.

Sometimes a sniper's bullet whirs
Or twangs the whining wire;
Sometimes a soldier sighs and stirs
As in hell's frying fire.

From out a high cool cloud descends
An aeroplane's far moan. . . .
The sun strikes down, the thin cloud rends . . .
The black speck travels on.

And sweating, dizzied, isolate
In the hot trench beneath,
We bide the next shrewd move of fate
Be it of life or death.

Robert Nichols

THE BOMBARDMENT

Slowly, without force, the rain drops into the city. It stops a moment on the carved head of Saint John, then slides on again, slipping and trickling over his stone cloak. It splashes from the lead conduit of a gargoyle, and falls from it in turmoil on the stones in the Cathedral square. Where are the people, and why does the fretted steeple sweep about in the sky? Boom! The sound swings against the rain. Boom, again! After it, only water rushing in the gutters, and the turmoil from the spout of the gargoyle. Silence. Ripples and mutters. Boom!

The room is damp, but warm. Little flashes swarm about from the firelight. The lusters of the chandelier are bright, and clusters of rubies leap in the bohemian glasses on the *étagère*. Her hands are restless, but the white masses of her hair are quite still. Boom! Will it never cease to torture, this iteration! Boom! The vibration shatters a glass on the *étagère*. It lies there, formless and glowing, with all its crimson gleams shot out of pattern, spilled, flowing red, blood-red. A thin bell-note pricks through the silence. A door creaks. The old lady speaks: "Victor, clear away that broken glass." "Alas! Madame, the bohemian glass!" "Yes, Victor, one hundred years ago my father brought it—" Boom! The room shakes, the servitor quakes. Another goblet shivers and breaks. Boom!

It rustles at the window-pane, the smooth, streaming rain, and he is shut within its clash and murmur. Inside is his candle, his table, his ink, his pen, and his dreams. He is thinking, and the walls are pierced with beams of sunshine, slipping through young green. A fountain tosses itself up at the blue sky, and through the spattered water in the basin he can see copper carp, lazily floating among cold leaves. A wind-harp in a cedar-tree grieves and whispers, and words blow into his brain, bubbled, iridescent, shooting up like flowers of fire, higher and higher. Boom! The flame-flowers snap on their slender stems. The fountain rears up in long broken spears of dishevelled water and flattens into the earth. Boom! And there is only the room, the table, the candle, and the sliding rain. Again, Boom!—Boom!—Boom! He stuffs his fingers into his ears. He sees corpses, and cries out in fright. Boom! It is night, and they are shelling the city! Boom! Boom!

A child wakes and is afraid, and weeps in the darkness. What has made the bed shake? "Mother, where are you? I am awake." "Hush, my darling, I am here." "But, Mother, something so queer happened, the room shook." Boom! "Oh! What is it? What is the matter?" Boom! "Where is Father? I am so afraid." Boom! The child sobs and shrieks. The house trembles and creaks. Boom!

Retorts, globes, tubes and phials lie shattered. All his trials oozing across the floor. The life that was his choosing, lonely, urgent, goaded by a hope, all gone. A weary man in a ruined laboratory, that is his story. Boom! Gloom and ignorance, and the jig of drunken brutes. Disease like snakes crawling over the earth, leaving trails of slime. Wails from people burying their dead. Through

124

the window, he can see the rocking steeple. A ball of fire falls on the lead of the roof, and the sky tears apart on a spike of flame. Up the spire, behind the lacings of stone, zigzagging in and out of the carved tracings, squirms the fire. It spouts like yellow wheat from the gargoyles, coils round the head of Saint John, and aureoles him in light. It leaps into the night and hisses against the rain. The Cathedral is a burning stain on the white, wet night.

Boom! The Cathedral is a torch, and the houses next to it begin to scorch. Boom! The bohemian glass on the *étagère* is no longer there. Boom! A stalk of flame sways against the red damask curtains. The old lady cannot walk. She watches the creeping stalk and counts. Boom!—Boom!—Boom!

The poet rushes into the street, and the rain wraps him in a sheet of silver. But it is threaded with gold and powdered with scarlet beads. The city burns. Quivering, spearing, thrusting, lapping, streaming, run the flames. Over roofs and walls and shops, and stalls. Smearing its gold on the sky, the fire dances, lances itself through the doors, and lisps and chuckles along the floors.

The child wakes again and screams at the yellow petalled flower flickering at the window. The little red lips of flame creep along the ceiling beams.

The old man sits among his broken experiments and looks at the burning Cathedral. Now the streets are swarming with people. They seek shelter and crowd

into the cellar. They shout and call, and over all, slowly
and without force, the rain drops into the city. Boom!
And the steeple crashes down among the people. Boom!
Boom, again! The water rushes along the gutters. The
fire roars and mutters. Boom!

Amy Lowell

TO GERMANY

You are blind like us. Your hurt no man designed,
And no man claimed the conquest of your land.
But, gropers both through fields of thought confined,
We stumble and we do not understand.
You only saw your future bigly planned,
And we, the tapering paths of our own mind,
And in each other's dearest ways we stand,
And hiss and hate. And the blind fight the blind.

When it is peace, then we may view again
With new-won eyes each other's truer form,
And wonder. Grown more loving-kind and warm,
We'll grasp firm hands and laugh at the old pain,
When it is peace. But until peace the storm,
The darkness, and the thunder and the rain.

Charles Hamilton Sorley

AND THE COCK CREW

"I hate them all!" said old Gaspard,
  And in his weatherbeaten face
The lines of bitterness grew hard,

126

For he had seen his dwelling-place
Laid waste in very wantonness
And all his little treasures flung
Into that never-sated press
From which no wine, but gall, had sprung—
And not alone his heart was sore,
For in his frail old limbs he bore
Wounds of the heavy ruthless hand
That weighed so cruelly of late
Upon the people and the land.
It was not hard to understand
Whom old Gaspard should hate,
Even the German lad who lay
His neighbor in the hospital,
The boy who pleaded, night and day,
"Don't let me die! Don't let me die!
When I see the dawn, I know
I shall live out the day, and then
I'm not afraid . . . till dark . . . but oh,
How soon the night comes round again!
Don't let me die! Don't let me die!"

The old man muttered at each low,
Pitiful, half-delirious cry,
"They should die, had I the say,
In Hell's own torment, one and all!"
And then would drag himself away
Despite each motion's agony
To where the wounded poilus lay,
To cheer them with his mimicry
Of barnyard noises and his gay
Old songs of what life used to be.

One night the lad suddenly cried
"Mother!"   And though the sister knew,
He was so young, so terrified,
"You're safe—the east is light," she lied.
But "No!" he sobbed. "The cock must crow
Before the dawn—" They did not hear
A cripple crawl across the floor.
But all at once, outside the door
Within the courtyard, strong and clear,
Once, twice, and thrice, crew chanticleer.
The blue eyes closed, and the boy sighed,
"I'm not afraid, now day's begun.
I'll live . . . till . . ." with a smile, he died.

And in that hour when he denied
The god of hate, I think that One
Passed through the hospital's dark yard
And turning, looked on old Gaspard.

Amelia Josephine Burr

BILL'S GRAVE

I'm gatherin' flowers by the wayside to lay on the grave
of Bill;
I've sneaked away from the billet, 'cause Jim wouldn't
understand;
'E'd call me a silly fat'ead, and larf till it made 'im ill,
To see me 'ere in the cornfield, wiv a big bookay in me
'and.

For Jim and me we are rough uns, but Bill was one o'
the best;
We 'listed and learned together to larf at the wust wot
comes;
Then Bill copped a packet proper, and took 'is departure
West,
So sudden 'e 'adn't a minit to say good-bye to 'is chums.

And they took me to where 'e was planted, a sort of a
measly mound,
And thinks I 'ow Bill would be tickled, bein' so soft and
queer,
If I gathered a bunch o' them wild-flowers, and sort of
arranged them round
Like a kind of a bloody headpiece . . . and that's the
reason I'm 'ere.

But not for the love of glory I wouldn't 'ave Jim to know.
'E'd call me a slobberin' Cissy, and larf till 'is sides was
sore;
I'd 'ave laughed at meself too, it isn't so long ago;
But some'ow it changes a feller, 'avin' a taste o' war.

It 'elps a man to be 'elpful, to know wot 'is pals is worth;
(Them golden poppies is blazin' like lamps some fairy
'as lit);
I'm fond o' them big white dysies. . . . Now Jim's of the
salt o' the earth;
But 'e's got a tongue wot's a terror, and 'e ain't sentimental a bit.

I likes them blue chaps wot's 'idin' so shylike among the
corn.
Won't Bill be glad! We was allus thicker'n thieves, we
three.
Why! 'O's that singin' so 'earty? *Jim!* And as sure as
I'm born
'E's there in the giddy cornfields, a-gatherin' flowers like
me.

Quick! Drop me posy be'ind me. I watches 'im for a
while,
Then I says: "Wot 'o, there, Chummy! Wot price the
little bookay?"
And 'e starts like a bloke wot's guilty, and 'e says with a
sheepish smile,
"She's a bit of orl right, the widder wot keeps the
estaminay."

So 'e goes away in a 'urry, and I wishes 'im best o' luck,
And I picks up me bunch o' wild-flowers, and the light's
gettin' sort o' dim,
When I makes me way to the boneyard, and . . . I stares
like a man wot's stuck,
For wot do I see? *Bill's grave-mound strewn with the
flowers of Jim.*

Of course I won't never tell 'im, bein' a tactical lad;
And Jim parley-voos to the widder: "Trez beans, lamoor;
compree?"
Oh, 'e'd die of shame if 'e knew I knew; but say! won't
Bill be glad
When 'e stares through the bleedin' clods and sees the
blossoms of Jim and me? *Robert W. Service*

THE SOLDIER

If I should die, think only this of me:
   That there's some corner of a foreign field
That is forever England. There shall be
   In that rich earth a richer dust concealed;
A dust whom England bore, shaped, made aware,
   Gave, once, her flowers to love, her ways to roam,
A body of England's, breathing English air,
   Washed by the rivers, blest by suns of home.

And think, this heart, all evil shed away,
   A pulse in the eternal mind, no less
     Gives somewhere back the thoughts by England
       given;
Her sights and sounds; dreams happy as her day;
   And laughter, learnt of friends; and gentleness,
     In hearts at peace, under an English heaven.

Rupert Brooke

THE RETURN

He went, and he was gay to go;
And I smiled on him as he went.
My son—'twas well he couldn't know
My darkest dread, nor what it meant—

Just what it meant to smile and smile
And let my son go cheerily—
My son . . . and wondering all the while
What stranger would come back to me.

Wilfrid Wilson Gibson

DOES IT MATTER?

Does it matter?—losing your leg? . . .
For people will always be kind,
And you need not show that you mind
When the others come in after hunting
To gobble their muffins and eggs.

Does it matter?—losing your sight? . . .
There's such splendid work for the blind;
And people will always be kind,
As you sit on the terrace remembering
And turning your face to the light.

Do they matter?—those dreams from the pit? . . .
You can drink and forget and be glad,
And people won't say that you're mad;
For they'll know that you've fought for your country,
And no one will worry a bit.

Siegfried Sassoon

STEEL WINGS

Man has grown wings!—
Audacious, glorious, triumphing he springs
From the lap of his old foster-mother earth—
In youth and strength and pride and lusty mirth
Exultantly he flings
Her swaddling-bands of gravity aside,

132

Rends her cloud-wrappings, free at last to ride
The fallow fenceless acres of the skies—
Man has won wings, and flies.

Through centuries has grown his dream of flight—
Up! Up the sheer blue height!—
On wings of wax and feather,
Wings of cord and leather,
Of wood and canvas—till the sky-vaults peal
To roar of wings of steel
In glittering coveys whirring past—
Man has found wings at last.

With straining thought—with hazard, pain, and sweat—
With life-blood—man has made his wings—and yet—
He that has wings may aim toward a star,
Or swoop upon his enemy in war;
Above the nations shrills the witches' cry—
Up from below! Fly! Fly!
In furious swarms the death-mad harpies scud,
Flying for lust of blood;
Aloft in stainless air, above earth's ills,
Man spreads his wings, and kills.

Man flies at last—his mortal body scales
The steeps of space—fresh trails
Above the eagle-roads are his to seek;
What should he care if, dazed and weak,
His outstripped soul yet clings
To earth—has not man wings?—
To dare the wind in darts and swerves,
And spiral down in flashing curves?

If flesh and metal can do this, and more,
Why should his spirit soar?
Infinity, wider than wing can span,
Is all remains to man.
Far may steel wings explore
Limitless ether, and miss Paradise—
And while his earth-born body sweeps the skies
Man's earth-bound spirit dies.

Joan Ramsay

NEXT TO OF COURSE GOD

"next to of course god america i
love you land of the pilgrims' and so forth oh
say can you see by the dawn's early my
country 'tis of centuries come and go
and are no more what of it we should worry
in every language even deafanddumb
thy sons acclaim your glorious name by gorry
by jingo by gee by gosh by gum
why talk of beauty what could be more beautiful than those heroic happy dead
who rushed like lions to the roaring slaughter
they did not stop to think they died instead
then shall the voices of liberty be mute?"

He spoke. And drank rapidly a glass of water.

E. E. Cummings

Only a man harrowing clods
    In a slow silent walk,
With an old horse that stumbles and nods
    Half asleep as they stalk.

Only thin smoke without flame
    From the heaps of couch-grass:
Yet this will go onward the same
    Though Dynasties pass.

Yonder a maid and her wight
    Come whispering by;
War's annals will fade into night
    Ere their story die.

Thomas Hardy

CONTINUITY

No sign is made while empires pass,
The flowers and stars are still His care,
The constellations hid in grass,
The golden miracles in air.

Life in an instant will be rent,
Where death is glittering blind and wild—
The Heavenly Brooding is intent
To that last instant on Its child.

135

It breathes the glow in brain and heart,
Life is made magical. Until
Body and spirit are apart
The Everlasting works Its will.

In that wild orchid that your feet
In their next falling shall destroy,
Minute and passionate and sweet
The Mighty Master holds His joy.

Though the crushed jewels droop and fade,
The Artist's labors will not cease,
And of the ruins shall be made
Some yet more lovely masterpiece.

A. E.

PART FIVE

QUESTIONS AND SUGGESTIONS

Dulce et Decorum Est

Is the picture more horrible to you because the poet voices his own sense of horror? Does the personal, savage pointing of the "moral" in the last lines add to the effect?

Counter-Attack

Since the first word is "We," look through the poem to see whether or not you are reminded of the poet's presence as you were in the previous one. Are the last five words a forceful ending? Do you prefer the type of ending in "Dulce et Decorum Est" or not? Explain.

Refugees

Here is a purely objective picture given to us through dialogue. What lines might set a motion-picture writer to constructing a scenario? He doubtless would want to devise some ending. Why did not the poet give any?

An Open Boat

In what ways is this poem similar to "Refugees"? In what ways is it different? Which poem do you like the sound of better? Which one rouses more emotion? Would you rather have had a longer poem describing the torpedoing of the ship, the escape to the open boat, perhaps some brave deed of the lover which cost him his life?

Noon

When a description is to be simple and brief, how must the words be chosen? Illustrate your answer by picking out certain words about the trench, the aeroplane, and the men.

The Bombardment

It is especially important that this poem be read aloud to get the effect. Written in a form which Miss Lowell, its first user in English, christened "polyphonic prose," it lends itself wonderfully to either choral or solo reading. If the latter is done, why should the reader be someone with a deep voice?

Why is the series of pictures more effective in this case than a single picture would have been? What binds them together? Are all of them equally elaborate? Does the poem stop at the right point?

To Germany

Sorley—who was only nineteen when he wrote this—had spent several months in Germany the year before. (He was killed in action when he was twenty.) What is the probable connection between that stay and the mental attitude shown in these lines?

After the War, Sir Norman Angell wrote: "Wars are not made by wicked men knowing themselves to be wrong, but by good men passionately convinced on both sides that they are right." Compare this statement with Sorley's idea. Which is more abstract in its presentation, and which more concrete?

And the Cock Crew

Compare this poem with the preceding one. How has the concreteness been carried still further here? What previous poem in the group does it resemble in respect to the method of ending?

Bill's Grave

In creating a situation objectively, an author may present it as if he saw everything that concerned everybody in it, or he may limit himself to picturing it as it appeared to one person. Which was the method in "Refugees"? in "The Bombardment"? Which has Service employed here?

The Soldier

Is this the first purely subjective poem you have had in this group? What is the great advantage of the method? Is there any possible disadvantage?

Despite his presentiment of his coming death, Brooke would probably have been surprised to know the particular "corner of a foreign field" that was to be forever his and England's. Bound for the campaign in Gallipoli, he died of fever aboard the troop ship, and was buried on the island of Skyros, near Greece. In *The Glorious Adventure,* there is an account of Haliburton's visit to his grave, and a picture of it. The spot may yet become famous, for Brooke's reputation as a poet is steadily rising.

The Return

What line contains the whole punch of the poem? Write a brief list of things that the word "stranger" suggests to you.

Does It Matter?

Irony—usually classed as a figure of speech—is saying the opposite of what you mean in such a way that everybody ought to realize what you do mean. In speech, the tone of voice employed points the significance of even subtle irony. In writing, irony is more powerful when put in the form of a question. Why?

Do you think the poem was inspired by rage against war or against a by-product of war?

Steel Wings

Which part of the poem contains irony? Is it more or less effective than in "Does It Matter?" Explain.

Look back at the two other poems about flying. Which of the three do you like best? Tell why.

next to of course god

In the two previous poems you have seen examples of irony. Satire, which holds a person or custom up to ridicule in the hope of possible reform, is either ironical or direct.

What traits of the orator are satirized? How? Have you ever listened to orators like him? Do you know what the word "demagogue" means? What do demagogues do to people before war? in time of war? after war?

In Time of "The Breaking of Nations"

What gives these few lines their tremendous appeal to the imagination? Does any of it come through the ear?

Continuity

Why was it necessary to use direct statements, rather than subtle ones, to convey the meaning here? Which seems more poetical, the idea itself or the expression of the idea?

PART FIVE

SUGGESTED SUPPLEMENTARY READING

Older Poems

Agincourt	Michael Drayton
To Lucasta, on Going to the Wars	Richard Lovelace
Burial of Sir John Moore .	Charles Wolfe
Lament for Flodden . .	Jane Elliott
Gathering Song of Donald the Black	Sir Walter Scott
The Battle of Blenheim .	Robert Southey
Vigil Strange I Kept on the Field One Night . .	Walt Whitman
The Wound-Dresser . .	Walt Whitman
Roll-Call	Nathaniel Graham Shepherd
Keenan's Charge . . .	George Parsons Lathrop
The Old Man and Jim .	James Whitcomb Riley
Hohenlinden . . .	Thomas Campbell

Newer Poems

The Man He Killed . .	Thomas Hardy
Aftermath	Siegfried Sassoon
The Conquerors . . .	Harry Kemp
Christ in Flanders . .	Lucy Whitmell
Let Us Have Peace . .	Nancy Byrd Turner
Youth in Arms . . .	Harold Monro
The Dead	Rupert Brooke
Grass	Carl Sandburg
Thomas of the Light Heart .	Owen Seaman

Part Six

Our history is grave, noble, and tragic.

MacLeish

FOREWORD

The figures of man's past offer an absorbing field for study and reflection. We instinctively feel that in poetry describing them it is appropriate to use striking effects, to depart from the conventional and casual, and to make the "setup" rich in appeal to the ear. Only the simpler factors in sound were discussed in Part One; for the ones here we shall need a more detailed study.

You all have heard fine symphony orchestras over the radio. Why is the popularity of their programs growing every year? Because the rich embroidery of musical themes gives ever-increasing satisfaction to people who learn to listen for the different tones and melodies of the individual instruments. Similarly, if you will listen often enough for blending sounds and rhythm patterns, you will increase your enjoyment of "elaborate" poems. Metrical verse is capable of many variations: in length of line, in rhymes, and in the amount of pleasing irregularity. As for cadenced verse, no two pieces of it are ever like each other. Since it is hard to think of rhythm, whether in metrical or in cadenced poems, without the sound of words, a short study is given here of three frequently used word devices: assonance, alliteration, and onomatopoeia. All these things are being explained in order that you may realize how they make sound pleasing and may recognize them as old friends whenever they occur.

And speaking of radio, more and more programs of poetry-reading are being broadcast. Listen in on some of them; send in the titles of poems that you would like to hear read; and, if they are given, compare the rendering with your own.

IN THE CLIFF DWELLINGS

I

The cliffs of sandstone rise from gray to blue,
They face a desert, vast of flaming suns—
Their backs stand pressed in mountains . . . Here a few
Cliff windows, empty eyes of skeletons,
Blank and indifferent stare far away.
A tribe has long since passed from blue to gray
Of time and silence, and these empty caves
Against the sky are silent but for wind
Above the heat that spreads in dizzy waves
To distance where the misty veils are thinned
And snow-peaks pierce them through. Here winds may
    howl
And foxes, down the worn stone pathways, prowl
Above their desert foes, and scorn as friend
The basking lizard and high-roosting owl . . .
Beginning is not here. Was this the end?

II

What nomads of the north from glacial flow
Fled to this land and dug their caves in stone
Above the mark of waters? . . . All we know
Is what we find where once a nation, grown
To greatness, won the desert for its own.
There is a desert history that runs
Through endless drouth and madness of the suns
That melted and poured down upon the land
Such pestilence of fire and flaming breath
That living things turned molten with the sand,

And over all was hiss of heat and death . . .
Here is no nation left in skeletons,
For bones are seldom found—but bowls of corn
And bins for grain and deep-worn grinding stones
Are in the cliff-rooms. Paintings yet adorn
The smoke-streaked walls. Past each high window
    moans
The wind that tells us nothing. Even bones
Were smashed or melted in that nameless strife.
About us blows the dust, above are blown
Wild clouds and we are chilled near the Unknown.

III

A tribal music leaped upon these airs
Blown up the canyon where the river sprayed
Its falls against the stars. . . . It comes again
Upon the rise and fall of wind that bears
A mystery of sound, as when were played
The joys and longings of the desert men.
O Tribe of Sun, at last by sun betrayed,
By earth-gods left deserted to a fate
Of flame blown into deep oblivion!
Fallen are gongs that greeted rising sun—
And only Desert wears the robes of State!
Pale purple mantles of the distance fall
From tawny shoulders of each grim-faced height.
The ruby, opal and the amethyst
Flash from the anklets of the watchers tall
And mighty, lonely and aloof in might—
Stern through half-parted curtains of the mist.
In hushed assemblage near the sky they stand
About vast empty circles of the sand.

Men make a pilgrimage from every land
To follow traces through these cavern rooms,
And look on things they cannot understand:
The signs of life that passed, these lights and glooms
Of desert, but they feel some mood of these
That gives them sense of wild lands' mysteries.
They have the sense of passing from the things
That they have known, and nearer the unknown
Trace out fantastic figures on the stone,
Serpents and birds with distance on their wings.
And men lift grains and corn that in the bin
Were stored while Age went out and Age came in,
And finger over grinding stones, deep worn
Before the Sphinx's face was flushed with morn.
And, here and there, they find a garment spun—
Of linen soft as cloth blessed to adorn
The Queen of Sheba pleasing Solomon. . . .
From room to room they pass, and in their eyes
Is such a look as comes when, at the rim
Of lofty cliffs, one stops before the skies
And feels the haze of distance grapple him.

v

The workmen dig in sands all up and down
A narrow valley to uncover walls
Of one great house, within itself a town,
And over them the glare of sunlight falls
As once it fell on other men who toiled
With other dreams, and by some fate were foiled
At last and left no trace across the sands.

We may restore lost cities of these lands
And build new pathways to the cliff-rooms high
Above the valley, and come here to dream . . .
The dreams will be our own. . . . The springs are dry.
The dead leaves drift on bleached sands where a stream
Once marked the cliff, and passed with desert men.
We cannot bring the glory back again
In tribes victorious against their foes
An Age—now Ages gone. The cactus grows
Where some proud chieftain of the desert stood . . .
The Desert now is king. A cedar wood
Against the sky lifts where the corridors
Of his vast temple start and, roofed with blue
And walled with haze of rainbows, reach great rooms
Of glowing light, and then pass onward through
Mirage to distance of the chasmed glooms,
Where Space, like mist, drifts through the last hushed
    doors.

Glenn Ward Dresbach

HE FELL AMONG THIEVES

"Ye have robbed," said he, "ye have slaughtered and made
    an end,
    Take your ill-got plunder, and bury the dead:
What will ye more of your guest and sometime friend?"
    "Blood for our blood," they said.

He laughed: "If one may settle the score for five,
    I am ready; but let the reckoning stand till day:

148

I have loved the sunlight as dearly as any alive."
  "You shall die at dawn," said they.

He flung his empty revolver down the slope,
  He climbed alone to the Eastward edge of the trees;
All night long in a dream untroubled of hope
  He brooded, clasping his knees.

He did not hear the monotonous roar that fills
  The ravine where the Yassîn river sullenly flows;
He did not see the starlight on the Laspur hills,
  Or the far Afghan snows.

He saw the April noon on his books aglow,
  The wisteria trailing in at the window wide;
He heard his father's voice from the terrace below
  Calling him down to ride.

He saw the gray little church across the park,
  The mounds that hide the loved and honoured dead;
The Norman arch, the chancel softly dark,
 •The brasses black and red.

He saw the School Close, sunny and green,
  The runner beside him, the stand by the parapet wall,
The distant tape, and the crowd roaring between,
  His own name over all.

He saw the dark wainscot and timbered roof,
  The long tables, and the faces merry and keen;
The College Eight and their trainer dining aloof,
  The Dons on the dais serene.

He watched the liner's stem ploughing the foam,
  He felt her trembling speed and the thrash of her
    screw;
He heard her passengers' voices talking of home,
  He saw the flag she flew.

And now it was dawn. He rose strong on his feet,
  And strode to his ruined camp below the wood;
He drank the breath of the morning cool and sweet;
  His murderers round him stood.

Light on the Laspur hills was broadening fast,
  The blood-red snow-peaks chilled to a dazzling white;
He turned, and saw the golden circle at last,
  Cut by the eastern height.

"O glorious Life, Who dwellest in earth and sun,
  I have lived, I praise and adore Thee."
                              A sword swept.
Over the pass the voices one by one
  Faded, and the hill slept.

                              Henry Newbolt

THE CREATION

And God stepped out on space,
And he looked around and said:
I'm lonely—
I'll make me a world.

150

And far as the eye of God could see
Darkness covered everything,
Blacker than a hundred midnights
Down in a cypress swamp.

Then God smiled,
And the light broke,
And the darkness rolled up on one side,
And the light stood shining on the other,
And God said: That's good!

Then God reached out and took the light in his hands,
And God rolled the light around in his hands
Until he made the sun;
And he set that sun a-blazing in the heavens.
And the light that was left from making the sun
God gathered it up in a shining ball
And flung it against the darkness,
Spangling the night with the moon and stars.
Then down between
The darkness and the light
He hurled the world;
And God said: That's good!

Then God himself stepped down—
And the sun was on his right hand,
And the moon was on his left;
The stars were clustered about his head,
And the earth was under his feet.
And God walked, and where he trod
His footsteps hollowed the valleys out
And bulged the mountains up.

Then he stopped and looked and saw
That the earth was hot and barren.
So God stepped over to the edge of the world
And he spat out the seven seas—
He batted his eyes, and the lightnings flashed—
He clapped his hands, and the thunder rolled—
And the waters above the earth came down,
The cooling waters came down.

Then the green grass sprouted,
And the little red flowers blossomed,
The pine tree pointed his finger to the sky,
And the oak spread out his arms,
The lakes cuddled down in the hollows of the ground,
And the rivers ran down to the sea;
And God smiled again,
And the rainbow appeared,
And curled itself around his shoulder.

Then God raised his arm and he waved his hand
Over the sea and over the land,
And he said: Bring forth! Bring forth!
And quicker than God could drop his hand,
Fishes and fowls
And beasts and birds
Swam the rivers and the seas,
Roamed the forests and the woods,
And split the air with their wings.
And God said: That's good!

Then God walked around,
And God looked around

On all that he had made.
He looked at his sun,
And he looked at his moon,
And he looked at his little stars;
He looked on his world
With all its living things,
And God said: I'm lonely still.

Then God sat down—
On the side of a hill where he could think;
By a deep, wide river he sat down;
With his head in his hands,
God thought and thought,
Till he thought: I'll make me a man!

Up from the bed of the river
God scooped the clay;
And by the bank of the river
He kneeled him down;
And there the great God Almighty
Who lit the sun and fixed it in the sky,
Who flung the stars to the most far corner of the night,
Who rounded the earth in the middle of his hand;
This Great God,
Like a mammy bending over her baby,
Kneeled down in the dust
Toiling over a lump of clay
Till he shaped it in his own image;

Then into it he blew the breath of life,
And man became a living soul.
Amen. Amen.

James Weldon Johnson

LEPANTO

White founts falling in the Courts of the Sun,
And the Soldan of Byzantium is smiling as they run;
There is laughter like the fountains in that face of all
    men feared,
It stirs the forest darkness, the darkness of his beard,
It curls the blood-red crescent, the crescent of his lips,
For the inmost sea of all the earth is shaken with his
    ships.
They have dared the white republics up the capes of
    Italy,
They have dashed the Adriatic round the Lion of the
    Sea,
And the Pope has cast his arms abroad for agony and
    loss,
And called the kings of Christendom for swords about
    the Cross.
The cold Queen of England is looking in the glass;
The shadow of the Valois is yawning at the Mass;
From evening isles fantastical rings faint the Spanish
    gun,
And the Lord upon the Golden Horn is laughing in the
    sun.

Dim drums throbbing, in the hills half heard,
Where only on a nameless throne a crownless prince has
    stirred,
Where, risen from a doubtful seat and half attainted
    stall,
The last knight of Europe takes weapons from the wall,

The last and lingering troubadour to whom the bird has
    sung,
That once went singing southward when all the world
    was young.
In that enormous silence, tiny and unafraid,
Comes up along a winding road the noise of the Crusade.
Strong gongs groaning as the guns boom far,
Don John of Austria is going to the war,
Stiff flags straining in the night-blasts cold
In the gloom black-purple, in the glint old-gold,
Torchlight crimson on the copper kettle-drums,
Then the tuckets, then the trumpets, then the cannon,
    and he comes.
Don John laughing in the brave beard curled,
Spurning of his stirrups like the thrones of all the world,
Holding his head up for a flag of all the free.
Love-light of Spain—hurrah!
Death-light of Africa!
Don John of Austria
Is riding to the sea.

Mahound is in his paradise above the evening star,
(Don John of Austria is going to the war.)
He moves a mighty turban on the timeless houri's knees,
His turban that is woven of the sunsets and the seas.
He shakes the peacock gardens as he rises from his ease,
And he strides among the tree-tops and is taller than the
    trees,
And his voice through all the garden is a thunder sent
    to bring
Black Azrael and Ariel and Ammon on the wing.
Giants and the Genii,

Multiplex of wing and eye,
Whose strong obedience broke the sky
When Solomon was king.

They rush in red and purple from the red clouds of the
morn,
From temples where the yellow gods shut up their eyes
in scorn;
They rise in green robes roaring from the green hells of
the sea
Where fallen skies and evil hues and eyeless creatures be;
On them the sea-valves cluster and the grey sea-forests
curl,
Splashed with a splendid sickness, the sickness of the
pearl;
They swell in sapphire smoke out of the blue cracks of
the ground,—
They gather and they wonder and give worship to
Mahound.
And he saith, "Break up the mountains where the hermit-
folk can hide,
And shift the red and silver sands lest bone of saint abide,
And chase the Giaours flying night and day, not giving
rest,
For that which was our trouble comes again out of the
west.
We have set the seal of Solomon on all things under sun,
Of knowledge and of sorrow and endurance of things
done,
But a noise is in the mountains, in the mountains, and I
know

The voice that shook our palaces—four hundred years
    ago:
It is he that saith not 'Kismet'; it is he that knows not
    Fate;
It is Richard, it is Raymond, it is Godfrey in the gate!
It is he whose loss is laughter when he counts the wager
    worth,
Put down your feet upon him, that our peace be on the
    earth."
For he heard drums groaning and he heard guns jar,
(*Don John of Austria is going to the war.*)
Sudden and still—hurrah!
Bolt from Iberia!
Don John of Austria
Is gone by Alcalar.

St. Michael's on his Mountain in the sea-roads of the
    north
(*Don John of Austria is girt and going forth.*)
Where the grey seas glitter and the sharp tides shift
And the sea-folk labour and the red sails lift.
He shakes his lance of iron and he claps his wings of
    stone;
The noise is gone through Normandy; the noise is gone
    alone;
The North is full of tangled things and texts and aching
    eyes
And dead is all the innocence of anger and surprise,
And Christian killeth Christian in a narrow dusty room,
And Christian dreadeth Christ that hath a newer face of
    doom;

And Christian hateth Mary that God kissed in Galilee,
But Don John of Austria is riding to the sea.
Don John calling through the blast and the eclipse
Crying with the trumpet, with the trumpet of his lips,
Trumpet that sayeth ha!
　Domino gloria!
Don John of Austria
Is shouting to the ships.

King Philip's in his closet with the Fleece about his neck
(*Don John of Austria is armed upon the deck.*)
The walls are hung with velvet that is black and soft as
　sin,
And little dwarfs creep out of it and little dwarfs creep
　in.
He holds a crystal phial that has colours like the moon,
He touches, and it tingles, and he trembles very soon,
And his face is as a fungus of a leprous white and grey
Like plants in the high houses that are shuttered from
　the day,
And death is in the phial and the end of noble work,
But Don John of Austria has fired upon the Turk.
Don John's hunting and his hounds have bayed—
Booms away past Italy the rumour of his raid.
Gun upon gun, ha! ha!
Gun upon gun, hurrah!
Don John of Austria
Has loosed the cannonade.

The Pope was in his chapel before day or battle broke,
(*Don John of Austria is hidden in the smoke.*)

The hidden room in man's house where God sits all the
     year,
The secret window whence the world looks small and
     very dear.
He sees as in a mirror on the monstrous twilight sea
The crescent of the cruel ships whose name is mystery;
They fling great shadows foe-wards, making Cross and
     Castle dark,
They veil the plumed lions on the galleys of St. Mark;
And above the ships are palaces of brown, black-bearded
     chiefs,
And below the ships are prisons, where with multitudi-
     nous griefs,
Christian captives sick and sunless, all a labouring race
     repines
Like a race in sunken cities, like a nation in the mines.
They are lost like slaves that sweat, and in the skies of
     morning hung
The stairways of the tallest gods when tyranny was
     young.
They are countless, voiceless, hopeless as those fallen or
     fleeing on
Before the high King's horses in the granite of Babylon.
And many a one grows witless in his quiet room in hell
Where a yellow face looks inward through the lattice of
     his cell,
And he finds his God forgotten, and he seeks no more
     a sign—
(*But Don John of Austria has burst the battle-line!*)
Don John pounding from the slaughter-painted poop,
Purpling all the ocean like a bloody pirate's sloop,

Scarlet running over on the silvers and the golds,
Breaking of the hatches up and bursting of the holds,
Thronging of the thousands up that labour under sea
White for bliss and blind for sun and stunned for liberty.
Vivat Hispania!
Domino Gloria!
Don John of Austria
Has set his people free!

Cervantes on his galley sets the sword back in the sheath
(*Don John of Austria rides homeward with a wreath.*)
And he sees across a weary land a straggling road in
    Spain,
Up which a lean and foolish knight for ever rides in
    vain,
And he smiles, but not as Sultans smile, and settles back
    the blade. . . .
(*But Don John of Austria rides home from the Crusade.*)

Gilbert Keith Chesterton

CARGOES

Quinquireme of Nineveh from distant Ophir,
Rowing home to haven in sunny Palestine,
    With a cargo of ivory
    And apes and peacocks,
Sandalwood, cedarwood, and sweet white wine.

Stately Spanish galleon coming from the Isthmus,
Dipping through the Tropics by the palm-green shores

With a cargo of diamonds,
  Emeralds, amethysts,
Topazes, and cinnamon, and gold moidores.

Dirty British coaster with a salt-caked smoke stack,
Butting through the channel in the mad March days
  With a cargo of Tyne coal,
   Road rails, pig lead,
Firewood, ironware, and cheap tin trays.

John Masefield

FOR MAISTER GEOFFREY CHAUCER

A bard there was, and that a worthy wight,
Who, from the time that he began to write,
Served God and beauty with an humble mind,
And most of all he knew and loved mankind.
Laughing he was, and quick at many a jest,
The Lord loves mirth,—the devil take the rest!
A simple grace ere wine be poured at dinner,
A ready hand outstretched to saint and sinner,
A prayer at times, not lengthy but devout,
This was our poet's faith, without a doubt.
Travel he loved, and wonders had to tell
Of royal France and Italy as well,
And everywhere he went, his furtive pen
Took down the secrets of his fellow-men,
Their faces and their stories, high and low,
From lordly Petrarch and Boccaccio

Unto the meanest villein who could hold
A tavern audience with the tales he told.
But with his scrivening he never swerved
From duty to King Edward whom he served,
And though he roamed both France and Italy,
England was where he always longed to be,
And thither he returned with magic spoils
That England might have pleasure of his toils,
And hear his brave, chivalric stories sung
By English pilgrims in the English tongue.
Noble his spirit was, and gay his heart.
A judge of wine, a master of his art,
He loved all men, nor was ashamed to show it;
He was a very parfit gentil poet,
Gentil in life and parfit in his rhyme,—
God send us such another in our time!

Robert Silliman Hillyer

SONNET

There was an Indian, who had known no change,
    Who strayed content along a sunlit beach
Gathering shells. He heard a sudden strange
    Commingled noise; looked up; and gasped for speech.
For in the bay, where nothing was before,
    Moved on the sea, by magic, huge canoes,
With bellying cloths on poles, and not one oar,
    And fluttering colored signs and clambering crews.

162

And he, in fear, this naked man alone,
  His fallen hands forgetting all their shells,
His lips gone pale, knelt low behind a stone,
  And stared, and saw, and did not understand,
Columbus's doom-burdened caravels
  Slant to the shore, and all their seamen land.

                                        J. C. Squire

BALLAD OF NAN BULLEN

Nan Bullen's lovers were as many as her pearls,
Merriest and fairest of Queen Kateryn's waiting-girls;
She laughed them off and coaxed them on and led them
    all a dance,
Wyatt and young Brereton and grave Sieur Brantome of
    France,
Smeaton the dark lutanist and Percy the proud lord,
Wooing her with prayer and song, with poem and with
    sword:
But if her love was any man's yet still she looked more
    high—
For what of your true-love when the King himself goes
    by?

Nan Bullen's charming was a witch's or a fay's,
All the court danced after her those laughing nights and
    days;
Gleaming grace in pageantry and soft hand on the lute,
Wit like any sparkling star and voice like any flute,

Darkest eyes and slenderest waist and honey-sweetened
tongue.
All the golden armor of the careless and the young,
Light embrace beneath the trees, light love-talk on the
stairs,
And what can an old Queen do who has only her prayers?

Nan Bullen's power rose as high as hills are piled,
Power to break a rival's heart and starve a rival's child,
Power to spread her castle wide and set her kinsfolk high,
And make the haughty cardinals kneel down when she
trod by:
She rode in state along the streets in shining robe and
crown
To wed the great King Henry in the face of London-
Town,
She sat upon her chair of pride, a queen where he was
king—
For what can your love do but give you everything?

Nan Bullen's laughter it was hushed upon a day,
What a king has given you a king can take away;
Other eyes were brighter and another voice more sweet—
Docile and demure as doom came young Jane Seymour's
feet . . .
Of all Nan Bullen's glories there was nothing left or
known
But a frightened little baby daughter crying all alone—
For what are charm and song and mirth where sentinels
keep ward
And what's the help of beauty for a headsman's sword?

Margaret Widdemer

THE HOST OF THE AIR

O'Driscoll drove with a song
The wild duck and the drake,
From the tall and the tufted reeds
Of the drear Hart Lake.

And he saw how the reeds grew dark
At the coming of night tide,
And dreamed of the long dim hair
Of Bridget his bride.

He heard while he sang and dreamed
A piper piping away,
And never was piping so sad,
And never was piping so gay.

And he saw young men and young girls
Who danced on a level place
And Bridget his bride among them,
With a sad and a gay face.

The dancers crowded about him
And many a sweet thing said,
And a young man brought him red wine
And a young girl white bread.

But Bridget drew him by the sleeve
Away from the merry bands,
To old men playing at cards
With a twinkling of ancient hands.

The bread and the wine had a doom,
For these were the host of the air;
He sat and played in a dream
Of her long dim hair.

He played with the merry old men
And thought not of evil chance,
Until one bore Bridget his bride
Away from the merry dance.

He bore her away in his arms,
The handsomest young man there,
And his neck and his breast and his arms
Were drowned in her long dim hair.

O'Driscoll scattered the cards
And out of his dream awoke:
Old men and young men and young girls
Were gone like a drifting smoke;

But he heard high up in the air
A piper piping away,
And never was piping so sad,
And never was piping so gay.

William B. Yeats

THE GHOSTS OF THE BUFFALOES

Would I might rouse the Lincoln in you all,
That which is gendered in the wilderness
From lonely prairies and God's tenderness.

Imperial soul, star of a weedy stream,
Born where the ghosts of buffaloes still dream,
Whose spirit hoof-beats storm above his grave,
Above that breast of earth and prairie-fire—
Fire that freed the slave.

Last night at black midnight I woke with a cry,
The windows were shaking, there was thunder on high,
The floor was a-tremble, the door was a-jar,
White fires, crimson fires, shone from afar.
I rushed to the dooryard. The city was gone.
My home was a hut without orchard or lawn.
It was mud-smear and logs near a whispering stream,
Nothing else built by man could I see in my dream . . .
Then . . .
Ghost-kings came headlong, row upon row,
Gods of the Indians, torches aglow.

They mounted the bear and the elk and the deer,
And eagles gigantic, aged and sere,
They rode long-horn cattle, they cried "A-la-la."
They lifted the knife, the bow, and the spear,
They lifted ghost-torches from dead fires below,
The midnight made grand with a red-god charge,
A red-god show,
A red-god show,
"A-la-la, a-la-la, a-la-la, a-la-la."

With bodies like bronze, and terrible eyes
Came the rank and the file, with catamount cries,
Gibbering, yipping, with hollow-skull clacks,
Riding white bronchos with skeleton backs,

Scalp-hunters, beaded and spangled and bad,
Naked and lustful and foaming and mad,
Flashing primeval demoniac scorn,
Blood-thirst and pomp amid darkness reborn,
Power and glory that sleep in the grass
While the winds and the snows and the great rains pass.
They crossed the gray river, thousands abreast,
They rode in infinite lines to the west,
Tide upon tide of strange fury and foam,
Spirits and wraiths, the blue was their home,
The sky was their goal where the star-flags are furled,
And on past those far golden splendors they whirled.
They burned to dim meteors, lost in the deep.
And I turned in dazed wonder, thinking of sleep.

And the wind crept by
Along, unkempt, unsatisfied,
The wind cried and cried—
Muttered of massacres long past,
Buffaloes in shambles vast . . .
An owl said: "Hark, what is a-wing?"
I heard a cricket carolling,
I heard a cricket carolling,
I heard a cricket carolling.

Then . . .
Snuffing the lightning that crashed from on high
Rose royal old buffaloes, row upon row.
The lords of the prairie came galloping by.
And I cried in my heart "A-la-la, a-la-la,
A red-god show,
A red-god show,
A-la-la, a-la-la, a-la-la, a-la-la."

Buffaloes, buffaloes, thousands abreast,
A scourge and amazement, they swept to the west.
With black bobbing noses, with red rolling tongues,
Coughing forth steam from their leather-wrapped lungs,
Cows with their calves, bulls big and vain,
Goring the laggards, shaking the mane,
Stamping flint teeth, flashing moon eyes,
Pompous and owlish, shaggy and wise.
Like sea-cliffs and caves resounded their ranks
With shoulders like waves, and undulant flanks.
Tide upon tide of strange fury and foam,
Spirits and wraiths, the blue was their home,
The sky was their goal where the star-flags are furled,
And on past those far golden splendors they whirled.
They burned to dim meteors, lost in the deep,
And I turned in dazed wonder, thinking of sleep.

I heard a cricket's cymbals play,
A scarecrow lightly flapped his rags,
And a pan that hung by his shoulder rang,
Rattled and thumped in a listless way,
And now the wind in the chimney sang,
The wind in the chimney,
The wind in the chimney,
The wind in the chimney,
Seemed to say:—
"Dream, boy, dream,
If you anywise can.
To dream is the work
Of beast or man.
Life is the west-going dream-storm's breath,
Life is a dream, the sigh of the skies,

169

The breath of the stars, that nod on their pillows
With their golden hair mussed over their eyes."
The locust played on his musical wing,
Sang to his mate of love's delight.
I heard the whippoorwill's soft fret.
I heard a cricket carolling,
I heard a cricket carolling,
I heard a cricket say: "Good-night, good-night,
Good-night, good-night, . . . good-night."

Vachel Lindsay

FOUR PRELUDES ON PLAYTHINGS OF THE WIND

"The past is a bucket of ashes."

I

The woman named To-morrow
sits with a hairpin in her teeth
and takes her time
and does her hair the way she wants it
and fastens at last the last braid and coil
and puts the hairpin where it belongs
and turns and drawls: "Well, what of it?
My grandmother, Yesterday, is gone.
What of it? Let the dead be dead."

II

The doors were cedar
and the panels strips of gold

and the girls were golden girls
and the panels read and the girls chanted:
>We are the greatest city,
>the greatest nation:
>nothing like us ever was.

The doors are twisted on broken hinges.
Sheets of rain swish through on the wind
>where the golden girls ran and the panels
>read:
>We are the greatest city,
>the greatest nation,
>nothing like us ever was.

III

It has happened before.
Strong men put up a city and got
>a nation together,
And paid singers to sing and women
>to warble: We are the greatest city,
>the greatest nation,
>nothing like us ever was.

And while the singers sang
and the strong men listened
and paid the singers well
and felt good about it all,
>there were rats and lizards who listened
>. . . and the only listeners left now
>. . . are . . . the rats . . . and the lizards.

171

And there are black crows
crying, "Caw, caw,"
bringing mud and sticks
building a nest
over the words carved
on the doors where the panels were cedar
and the strips on the panels were gold
and the golden girls came singing:
>   We are the greatest city,
>   the greatest nation:
>   nothing like us ever was.

The only singers now are crows crying, "Caw, caw,"
And the sheets of rain whine in the wind and doorways.
And the only listeners now are . . . the rats . . . and
>   the lizards.

IV

The feet of the rats
scribble on the door sills;
the hieroglyphs of the rat footprints
chatter the pedigrees of the rats
and babble of the blood
and gabble of the breed
of the grandfathers and the great-grandfathers
of the rats.

And the wind shifts
and the dust on a door sill shifts
and even the writing of the rat footprints

tells us nothing, nothing at all
about the greatest city, the greatest nation
where the strong men listened
and the woman warbled: Nothing like us ever
was.

Carl Sandburg

PART SIX

QUESTIONS AND SUGGESTIONS

In the Cliff Dwellings

What line in the poem mentions approximately the age of Indian civilization in the Americas? What modern American hero contributed to the discovery of ruins similar to these?

Perhaps you already know how *iambic pentameter,* the most common meter in English, is made. If not, look at the line quoted again below to indicate the versification:

> As once / it fell / on oth- / er men / who toiled /

What can you discover about the syllables in each of the five divisions that we call *feet?* What irregularities might be introduced into lines to save the meter from monotony? See if you can find some irregular lines in the poem by reading it aloud in class (chorus), stressing the accents strongly for the first verse-paragraph, and then continuing naturally.

When unrhymed, iambic pentameter is called *blank verse.*

He Fell Among Thieves

What sort of man is the central figure in this poem? Had life given him all the things that a man ought to have? How did this man feel about it?

In the first three lines of each stanza you can continue your study of *iambic pentameter.* Does it sound more or less regular than it did in the previous poem? How does the division into stanzas make this particular poem more effective? Why did the poet choose to make a last line with only three accents—*trimeter,* as it is called?

Read aloud the first two lines of the fourth stanza. What do you notice about the sounds of the words?

The Creation

Suppose that you did not know that this was patterned on sermons preached to old-fashioned Negro congregations, what word near the end of the poem might tell you?

Read aloud the first chapter of Genesis in the King James version of the Bible. Try writing out a few lines of it as if it were poetry, and compare it with this retelling. What device pointed out in Part One is common to both?

Lepanto

The adjective "gorgeous" is much abused; but few others would describe the musical effects of the words in this poem, secured by abundance and variety of rhymes and three devices.

The most frequent, *alliteration,* you can define yourselves after reading aloud the following lines:

"In the gloom black-purple, in the glint old-gold"
"And he strides among the tree-tops and is taller than the trees"
"Splashed with a splendid sickness, the sickness of the pearl"

For the second, *assonance,* refer back to "The Ancient Beautiful Things," where you heard it at the ends of lines. See how it can run through lines like these:

"Black Azrael and Ariel and Ammon on the wing"
"Where fallen skies and evil hues and eyeless creatures be"
"White for bliss and blind for sun and stunned for liberty"

The third is *onomatopoeia.* What do you notice about the sounds of the italicized words in these next expressions?

"*Dim drums throbbing,* in the hills half-heard"
"They rise in green robes *roaring* from the green hells of the sea"

175

> "*Booms* away past Italy the rumour of his raid"
> "*Breaking* of the hatches up and *bursting* of the holds"

Why would the poem be good for choral reading? Work out a scheme for solos and choruses.

Cargoes

In this masterly miniature of three civilizations, what feature of modern civilization do you think Masefield meant to deplore? Is there anything to be said for "cheap tin trays"?

Metrically the poem is interesting for its use of *trochaic* feet. (A *trochee,* like an iambus, has two syllables; but the accent comes on the first.) Trochees are often used throughout short lines, or introduced into iambic lines for variety. It is rare, however, to see them throughout long lines. Notice how Masefield breaks their rhythm just enough in each stanza—how?

For Maister Geoffrey Chaucer

Judging from this description of Chaucer, was he a poet in Flecker's sense of the word? (Read again "To a Poet a Thousand Years Hence.")

The poem is written in the meter of *The Canterbury Tales.* Ask your teacher to read you some lines from the Prologue, and then the description of the Knight.

Sonnet

Next to the rhymed pentameter couplet used by Chaucer (later called *heroic couplet*) and blank verse, the *sonnet* is the oldest set form used by English poets. (The *ballad stanza,* older than any, appealed only to the common people at first.) The sonnet was "imported" from Italy. What is the number of the lines? The meter of the lines? Notice the division between the first eight lines (the *octave*) and the last six (the *sestet*). Can you see any reason for the division?

The matter of different rhyme-combinations in sonnets is taken up in the Reference List. Consult it, and then, if you care to, turn back to work out the rhyme-schemes of the sonnets so far.

Ballad of Nan Bullen

Histories have changed the spelling of this lady's name and eschewed her nickname. Why did the poet go back to the old forms? (Read the poem again for its general tone.)

One metrical device contributes a great deal to the light, gay effect. It is in the first foot of the majority of lines. See if you can figure it out, remembering that the metrically correct pattern for the ballad is iambic.

The single seven-accent line corresponds to the first two lines in a regular ballad-stanza. Refer to "Song" (Part One).

The Host of the Air

In old days Irish peasants had many superstitions concerning the "Sidhe" or "host of the air." Immortal, invisible, "as many as the blades of grass," they were supposed to hover around strong young men or beautiful young women, trying to bewitch them and carry them away from earth.

Does O'Driscoll's dream make you fancy a possible disaster to his bride, or does it seem mere unconscious recollection of the old superstition?

Do you like the very simple verse-form? Is it a ballad?

The Ghosts of the Buffaloes

Look back to the note on "General William Booth."

Something of the variety in Lindsay's delivery might be suggested if the poem was read aloud by five pupils with different types of voices. Into what sections does it fall?

Pick out instances of alliteration and onomatopoeia.

"Sic transit gloria mundi" ("Thus passes the glory of the world"). Which word in that old saying comes nearest to "The past is a bucket of ashes"? Which word gives another idea that is brought out in the poem?

All the sections should be read aloud by a single person, teacher or pupil, who knows something about *free verse* (or *cadenced verse,* as some poets prefer to call it). Comparatively new to English, it has been used for years in other languages. It has no prevailing foot, no prescribed length of line, no regular stanza-divisions. Its beauty depends upon phrases, sentences, and groups of phrases and sentences constructed in such a way that when they are read aloud well the voice must rise, pause or hurry, and fall again in harmonious and varied cadences. Its defenders claim that it not only enables the poet to get musical effects, but also affords him a far wider choice of words than is possible in conventional verse.

Pick out four fine examples of onomatopoeia.

Why has this poem been put last in the group?

PART SIX

SUGGESTED SUPPLEMENTARY READING

Older Poems

Chevy Chase	Old Ballad
Sir Patrick Spens	Old Ballad
Ozymandias	Percy Bysshe Shelley
A Musical Instrument	Elizabeth Barrett Browning
Dream of Fair Women	Alfred Tennyson
King Robert of Sicily	Henry Wadsworth Longfellow
Dorothy Q.	Oliver Wendell Holmes
In Galilee	Mary Frances Butts
Sesostris	Lloyd Mifflin
Khamsin	Clinton Scollard

Newer Poems

Eve	Ralph Hodgson
The Wife of Llew	Francis Ledwidge
After Calvary	James M. Duff
A Song of Sherwood	Alfred Noyes
A Lady Comes to an Inn	Elizabeth J. Coatsworth
Drake's Drum	Henry Newbolt
The Explorer	Rudyard Kipling
The Lincoln Child	James Oppenheim
Gunga Din	Rudyard Kipling
Patterns	Amy Lowell

Part Seven

I tell thee Love is Nature's second sun.

Chapman

FOREWORD

"It is difficult to find words when one really has something to say. And even if one knows the right words, then one is ashamed to say them. All these words belong to other, earlier centuries. Our time has not the words yet to express its feelings. We can only be offhand—anything else rings false."

The modern attitude thus described by Remarque in *Three Comrades* voices a reason why many young people balk at reading any kind of poetry that expresses sentiment. You realize, as older people do, that deep and true feelings for others are the best stuff of which life is made; but you are not so sure that poets can express those feelings without "ringing false" and spoiling everything.

It is true that not so long ago all but the best love poetry was sickeningly sweet. Nowadays, however, poets have come to realize the value of three things in expressing sentiment. First comes their own sincerity. Long ago Sir Philip Sidney said, "Look in thy heart and write." Second, restraint, the art of holding back, of suggesting part of what one wants to say. And third, some freshness in expression, the avoidance, so far as possible, of the outworn phrases that we call clichés, and the use of words or figures that are simple and strong.

If you think that the poems in this section do not rate high in these three respects, try to find other love poems that do, to your mind, ring true. There will be many times in your life when you will obtain deep satisfaction from poems expressing genuine sentiment in what one might call universal language.

HASTINGS MILL

As I went down by Hastings Mill I lingered in my going
To smell the smell of piled-up deals and feel the salt wind
    blowing,
To hear the cables fret and creak and the ropes stir and
    sigh
(Shipmate, my shipmate!) as in days gone by.

As I went down by Hastings Mill I saw a ship there lying,
About her tawny yards the little clouds of sunset flying,
And half I took her for the ghost of one I used to know
(Shipmate, my shipmate!) many years ago.

As I went down by Hastings Mill I saw while I stood
    dreaming
The flicker of her riding light along the ripples streaming,
The bollards where we made her fast and the berth where
    she did lie
(Shipmate, oh shipmate!) in the days gone by.

As I went down by Hastings Mill I heard a fellow sing-
    ing,
Chipping off the deep-sea rust above the tide a-swinging;
And well I knew the queer old tune and well the song
    he sung
(Shipmate, my shipmate!) when the world was young.

And past the rowdy Union Wharf, and by the still tide
    sleeping,
To a randy, dandy deep-sea tune my heart in time was
    keeping,

To the thin, far sound of a shadowy watch a-hauling,
And the voice of one I knew across the high tide calling
(Shipmate, my shipmate!) and the late dusk falling.

Cicely Fox Smith

MY FRIEND

The friend I love is like the sea to me,
With spacious days of large tranquillity
When on my heart his wordless comforts lie,
As on the utter sea rim rests the sky;
And like the sea for wrath he is, and strong
To launch his surges on the cliffs of Wrong;
But most I love him for his deep-sea spell
Of unguessed secrets that he may not tell:
So I have seen him stand and look afar
Beyond the twilight to the evening star,
And like the ocean's haunting lure to me,
Deep in his eyes I read a mystery:—
For he whose soul we fathom to the end
Becomes our servant then, and not our friend.

Walter Prichard Eaton

MAN AND DOG

Yon Terence O'Rourke has a dog called Tim
Who's for ever close at the heels of him.

Now Terence is more than a rogue and thief,
And to meet wid him is to meet wid grief.

He'd cabbage a fowl and fleece the poor
And wastle and poach in the Divil's own door.

Yet yon ould beagle loves yon dour man
As only a dog—or a woman—can.

So I'm thinkin', mayhap, there's a trace ov good
Conc'aled in Terence, or no dog could

Be wastin' his time on a murderin' lad
From his brogans up to his midriff bad.

*But I'll take me oath if there's good in the lout
'Tis only a hound could be nosin' it out!*

Arthur Stringer

DEFINITION

I search among the plain and lovely words
To find what the one word "Mother" means; as well
Try to define the tangled songs of birds;
The echo in the hills of one clear bell.
One cannot snare the wind, or catch the wings
Of shadows flying low across the wheat;
Ah, who can prison simple, natural things
That make the long days beautiful and sweet?

"Mother"—a word that holds the tender spell
Of all the dear essential things of earth;
A home, clean sunlit rooms, and the good smell
Of bread; a table spread; a glowing hearth.
And love beyond the dream of anyone. . . .
I search for words for her . . . and there are none.

Grace Noll Crowell

A MAN-CHILD'S LULLABY

Little groping hands that must learn the weight of labor,
   Little eyes of wonder that must learn to weep;
Mother is thy life now: that shall be to-morrow—
Time enough for trouble—time enough for sorrow—
      Now . . . sleep.

Little dumb lips that shall wake and make a woman,
   Little blind heart that shall know the worst and best;
Mother is thy love now: that shall be hereafter—
Time enough for joy, and time enough for laughter—
      Now . . . rest.

Little rosy body, new-born of pain and beauty,
   Little lonely soul new-risen from the deep;
Mother is thy world now, whole and satisfying—
Time enough for living—time enough for dying—
      Now . . . sleep.

Brian Hooker

RUFUS PRAYS

In the darkening church,
Where but a few had stayed,
At the Litany Desk
The idiot knelt and prayed.

Rufus, stunted, uncouth,
The one son of his mother:
"Eh, I'd sooner 'ave Rufie,"
She said, "than many another.

" 'E's so useful about the 'ouse
And so gentle as 'e can be
And 'e gets up early o' mornin's
To make me a cup o' tea."

The formal evensong
Had passed over his head:
He sucked his thumb, and squinted,
And dreamed, instead.

Now while the organ boomed
To few who still were there,
At the Litany Desk
The idiot made his prayer:

"Gawd bless Muther,
'N' make Rufie a good lad.
Take Rufie to Heaven,
'N' forgive him when he's bad.

187

" 'N' early mornin's in Heaven
'E'll make Muther's tea,
'N' a cup for the Lord Jesus
'N' a cup for Thee."

L. A. G. Strong

THE LOOK

Strephon kissed me in the spring,
    Robin in the fall,
But Colin only looked at me
    And never kissed at all.

Strephon's kiss was lost in jest,
    Robin's lost in play,
But the kiss in Colin's eyes
    Haunts me night and day.

Sara Teasdale

LA VIE C'EST LA VIE

On summer afternoons I sit
Quiescent by you in the park,
And idly watch the sunbeams gild
And tint the ash-trees' bark.

Or else I watch the squirrels frisk
And chaffer in the grassy lane;

And all the while I mark your voice
Breaking with love and pain.

I know a woman who would give
Her chance of heaven to take my place;
To see the love-light in your eyes,
The love-glow on your face!

And there's a man whose lightest word
Can set my chilly blood afire;
Fulfillment of his least behest
Defines my life's desire.

But he will none of me, nor I
Of you.   Nor you of her.   'Tis said
The world is full of jests like these.—
I wish that I were dead.

Jessie Redmond Fauset

INNAMORATA

Happy in love was the bold Venetian sailor,
  Who, though he wooed in vain, could still prevail;
For when the maid denied him, with love to guide him,
  He painted her glowing face upon the sail.

"Be thou my love," he cried, "I have no other!"
  Voyaging on to many a far-off place
Where ships were hung with flags and royal emblems,
  He came under one sign, a maiden's face.

"Who is this?" cried the Greeks, and the Neapolitans,
  "A saint of our Lady!" they cried, and the men of
    Spain
Doffed their caps; but the yellow beards of Flanders
  Growled, "Only a fool."—And he sailed away again.

Scudding blithely over the glittering water,
  "Worthy art thou," he sang, "to face the sun."
Pale by night through the stars her face went rushing,
  "Worthy of heaven," he sang, "beloved one."

Cloud-burst and waterspout could not confound him;
  She rode on high—he dared the on-driving wave.
Love, I would be as the bold Venetian sailor,
  Ever one face keeping me true and brave.

W. Force Stead

WHY HE LOVES HER

For your copper hair
  And dryad ears,
    A forehead wise,
      And a nose that crinkles:

Cheeks that wear
  No trace of years,
    And two blue eyes
      Like periwinkles:

For things you say,
    And thoughts you keep:
        For your heart that sings
            What matter the season:

For the cunning way
    You curl asleep—
        For all these things,
            And for no good reason.

Norman R. Jaffray

BREAD AND WINE

From death of star to new star's birth,
    This ache of limb, this throb of head,
This sweaty shop, this smell of earth,
    For this we pray, "Give daily bread."

Then tenuous with dreams the night,
    The feel of soft brown hands in mine,
Strength from your lips for one more fight:
    Bread's not so dry when dipped in wine.

Countée Cullen

ANSWER

When all my questions drop like frozen birds
Into the dark recesses of my mind,
When I am stripped quite naked of soft words

And know myself as lame and halt and blind;
When truths that seemed most certain slip away
Like water or bright entities of sand,
When order comes to chaos in a day
And time is but a riddle to be scanned,

You are the answer merciful to hear,
You are a stream of bells across my sky,
You are the rich return for every fear
And every doubt. You are the deep reply;
And will be, always, till the question's done
And lovers rest compounded into one.

Virginia Moore

PSALM TO MY BELOVED

Lo, I have opened unto you the wide gates of my being,
And like a tide you have flowed into me.
The innermost recesses of my spirit are full of you, and
    all the channels of my soul are grown sweet with
    your presence.
For you have brought me peace;
The peace of great tranquil waters, and the quiet of the
    summer sea.
Your hands are filled with peace as the noon-tide is filled
    with light; about your head is bound the eternal
    quiet of the stars, and in your heart dwells the calm
    miracle of twilight.
I am utterly content.

In all my spirit is no ripple of unrest.
For I have opened unto you the wide gates of my being
And like a tide you have flowed into me.

Eunice Tietjens

A LYNMOUTH WIDOW

He was straight and strong, and his eyes were blue
As the summer meeting of sky and sea,
And the ruddy cliffs had a colder hue
Than flushed his cheek when he married me.

We passed the porch where the swallows breed,
We left the little brown church behind,
And I leaned on his arm, though I had no need,
Only to feel him so strong and kind.

One thing I never can quite forget;
It grips my throat when I try to pray—
The keen salt smell of a drying net
That hung on the churchyard wall that day.

He would have taken a long, long grave—
A long, long grave, for he stood so tall . . .
Oh, God, the crash of a breaking wave,
And the smell of the nets on the churchyard wall!

Amelia Josephine Burr

THE PENALTY OF LOVE

If Love should count you worthy, and should deign
　One day to seek your door and be your guest,
　Pause! ere you draw the bolt and bid him rest,
If in your old content you would remain.
For not alone he enters: in his train
　Are angels of the mists, the lonely quest,
　Dreams of the unfulfilled and unpossessed,
And sorrow, and Life's immemorial pain.

He wakes desires you never may forget,
　He shows you stars you never saw before,
　He makes you share with him, for evermore,
The burden of the world's divine regret.
How wise were you to open not!—and yet,
　How poor if you should turn him from the door.

Sidney Royse Lysaght

QUESTIONS AND SUGGESTIONS

Hastings Mill

(In Vancouver—this poet writes not only of the sea but of the northern Pacific Coast—great lumber mills line part of the harbor.)

The old sailor expresses his love for ships without much reserve; his longing for the friend he loved many years ago is conveyed by suggestion and restraint. Which appeals to you more, and why?

My Friend

Is the simile unusual? Are the points of comparison valid? Do you like the idea of some reserves between friends or not? Do you think that the type of person who restrains himself would like restraint in poetry?

Man and Dog

Why is this an unusual way of suggesting the truth that any real love enables one to see beneath the surface? What double purpose do the italicized words serve?

Definition

The ordinary person is inarticulate in the face of deep feeling. Should a poet be? Although she confesses failure to find exact words, this author has conveyed her meaning in two other ways. What are they?

A Man-Child's Lullaby

"Mother is thy world now, whole and satisfying." Why is it inevitable that there should be a streak of selfishness in mother-love, unless the mother realizes and conquers it? What shows that this mother probably will let her child go his way for himself?

Brian Hooker loves music; he has composed the librettos for many successful light operas. Does this sound "singable"? What is indicated by the row of dots after "Now"?

Rufus Prays

After the first agony of realizing that a child is not normal has dulled a little, mother-love must set itself to a long task. What three things has this mother succeeded in doing for her idiot son? Notice the art with which each is suggested.

The Look

State briefly the trait of human nature that makes this poem ring so true. Would it apply to other things besides a kiss? Do you see the reason why the lovers are given names from pastoral poetry? (If you don't know what the term *pastoral* means, you ought to. Look it up.)

La Vie C'est La Vie

Is the power of this poem due to the situation with which it deals, or to the words in which the situation is outlined? Would you like to see the poem condensed still further, perhaps to the same length as "The Look"?

Innamorata

Contrast the idea and characterization of this Renaissance love-story with the idea and characterization of the previous poem. What lines show that the author thinks it has an application to modern life? Do you like having the application made, or could you infer it?

196

Why He Loves Her

What does this do for us that none of the previous three poems has done? Which of these adjectives should you use to describe the diction: stately, elaborate, conventional, informal, original, labored? Does the last line remind you of any other poem in this group?

Bread and Wine

What elements are emphasized in this man's love for his wife? What makes the poem sincere? Had the two people in "Why He Loves Her" shared any hard times and troubles?

Answer

Again the loved one is spoken of as a refuge and a source of strength—but in what kind of trouble?

Since the diction of this poem depends for its effect largely on figures, examine these for their degree of freshness and exactness.

Psalm to My Beloved

In some recent versions of the Bible, the Psalms are printed as they should be, in the form of poetry. Why was it a good idea to model this poem on their long, flowing cadences? What do you notice about the words used?

A Lynmouth Widow

Suggestion and restraint are valuable chiefly because each reader fills them in according to his own personality. Have several people write out this story briefly in prose, and see how much they differ. But all should include one thing that the poet has emphasized. What is it?

The Penalty of Love

Have any other poems in this group dealt with the idea of love's *penalty*? Would you say that that was the main idea of the poem?

Is the poem more or less effective because the statements are general?

Is there such a thing as timeless diction in poetry? Or can you always distinguish modern ways of expression from older ones?

PART SEVEN

SUGGESTED SUPPLEMENTARY READING

Older Poems

"Let me not to the marriage of true minds"	William Shakespeare
Advice to a Girl	Thomas Campion
Sephestia's Song to Her Child .	Robert Greene
"My true love hath my heart" .	Sir Philip Sidney
Duncan Gray	Robert Burns
She Walks in Beauty . . .	George Gordon, Lord Byron
To Helen	Edgar Allan Poe
Annabel Lee	Edgar Allan Poe
The Courtin'	James Russell Lowell
"Heart, we will forget him" . .	Emily Dickinson

Newer Poems

Wee Hughie	Elizabeth Shane
The Old Nurse	Frances Cornford
Songs for My Mother . .	Anna Hempstead Branch
Two Who've Taken Trails To-gether	Mary Carolyn Davies
Mia Carlotta	T. A. Daly
Where Love Is	Amelia Josephine Burr
Spring Night	Sara Teasdale
"Once more into my arid days" .	Edna St. Vincent Millay

Part Eight

Life and death upon one tether
And running beautiful together.

Coffin

FOREWORD

To watch a skilled actor "making up" is fascinating. Even if his part does not call for a putty nose or a beard or a wig, he can do unbelievable things to his face by the use of rouge and a few "liners." Or instead of making himself into a different personality, he can high-light his own by a few simple tricks. In fact, everyone who appears in public has to learn that effects seldom carry unless in some way they are accentuated.

Similarly, most poets have learned how to use the various methods of expression that accentuate the underlying intensity of a poem. The aim of this section is to point out a few of the most common methods, such as climax, exaggeration, surprise, contrast, understatement, different forms of repetition, and the use of allusions, symbols, and sustained comparisons.

How far is a poet conscious of using technical methods deliberately to obtain certain effects? Probably there are as many different shades of this deliberateness as there are poets. But any emotion, to be artistically effective, must be under some degree of control; if it is not, it becomes either unreal or sentimental. Artistic control is manifested by a poet's skill in finding and using just the devices that will drive his point home.

CRYSTAL MOMENT

Once or twice this side of death
Things can make one hold his breath.

From my boyhood I remember
A crystal moment of September.

A wooded island rang with sounds
Of church bells in the throats of hounds.

A buck leaped out and took the tide
With jewels flowing past each side.

With his high head like a tree
He swam within a yard of me.

I saw the golden drop of light
In his eye turned dark with fright.

I saw the forest's holiness
On him like a fierce caress.

Fear made him lovely past belief,
My heart was trembling like a leaf.

He leaned towards the land and life
With need above him like a knife.

In his wake the hot hounds churned,
They stretched their muzzles out and yearned.

They bayed no more, but swam and throbbed,
Hunger drove them till they sobbed.

Pursued, pursuers reached the shore
And vanished. I saw nothing more.

So they passed, a pageant such
As only gods could witness much,

Life and death upon one tether
And running beautiful together.

Robert P. Tristram Coffin

DEATH AND GENERAL PUTNAM

His iron arm had spent its force,
No longer might he rein a horse;
Lone, beside the dying blaze
Dreaming dreams of younger days
       Sat old Israel Putnam.

Twice he heard, then three times more
A knock upon the oaken door,
A knock he could not fail to know,
That old man in the ember-glow.
       "Come," said General Putnam.

The door swung wide; in cloak and hood
Lean and tall the pilgrim stood
And spoke in tones none else might hear,

"Once more I come to bring you Fear!"
　　"Fear?" said General Putnam.

"You know not Fear?　And yet this face
Your eyes have seen in many a place
Since first in stony Pomfret, when
You dragged the mad wolf from her den."
　　"Yes," said General Putnam.

"Was I not close, when, stripped and bound
With blazing fagots heaped around
You heard the Huron war-cry shrill?
Was I not close at Bunker Hill?"
　　"Close," said General Putnam.

"Am I not that which strong men dread
On stricken field or fevered bed
On gloomy trail and stormy sea,
And dare you name my name to me?"
　　"Death," said General Putnam.

"We have been comrades, you and I,
In chase and war beneath this sky;
And now, whatever Fate may send,
Old comrade, can you call me friend?"
　　"Friend!" said General Putnam.

Then up he rose, and forth they went
Away from battleground, fortress, tent,
Mountain, wilderness, field and farm,
Death and the General, arm-in-arm,
　　Death and General Putnam.

Arthur Guiterman

TO AN ATHLETE DYING YOUNG

The time you won your town the race
We chaired you through the market-place;
Man and boy stood cheering by,
And home we brought you shoulder-high.

To-day, the road all runners come,
Shoulder-high we bring you home,
And set you at your threshold down,
Townsman of a stiller town.

Smart lad, to slip betimes away
From fields where glory does not stay,
And early though the laurel grows
It withers quicker than the rose.

Eyes the shady night has shut
Cannot see the record cut,
And silence sounds no worse than cheers
After earth has stopped the ears:

Now you will not swell the rout
Of lads that wore their honours out,
Runners whom renown outran
And the name died before the man.

So set, before its echoes fade,
The fleet foot on the sill of shade,
And hold to the low lintel up
The still-defended challenge-cup.

And round that early-laurelled head
Will flock to gaze the strengthless dead,
And find unwithered on its curls
The garland briefer than a girl's.

A. E. Housman

THE SEED SHOP

Here in a quiet and dusty room they lie,
Fated as crumbled stone or shifting sand,
Forlorn as ashes, shrivelled, scentless, dry—
Meadows and gardens running through my hand.

Dead that shall quicken at the trump of spring,
Sleepers to stir beneath June's morning kiss,
Though bees pass over, unremembering,
And no bird seek here bowers that were his.

In this brown husk a dale of hawthorn dreams;
A cedar in this narrow cell is thrust
That will drink deeply of a century's streams;
These lilies shall make summer on my dust.

Here in their safe and simple house of death,
Celled in their shells, a million roses leap;
Here I can blow a garden with my breath,
And in my hand a forest lies asleep.

Muriel Stuart

RICHARD CORY

Whenever Richard Cory went down town,
  We people on the pavement looked at him:
He was a gentleman from sole to crown,
  Clean favored, and imperially slim.

And he was always quietly arrayed,
  And he was always human when he talked;
But still he fluttered pulses when he said,
    "Good-morning," and he glittered when he walked.

And he was rich—yes, richer than a king,
  And admirably schooled in every grace:
In fine, we thought that he was everything
  To make us wish that we were in his place.

So on we worked, and waited for the light,
  And went without the meat and cursed the bread;
And Richard Cory, one calm summer night,
  Went home and put a bullet through his head.

Edwin Arlington Robinson

THE HORSE THIEF

There he moved, cropping the grass at the purple canyon's lip.
  His mane was mixed with the moonlight that silvered his snow-white side,

For the moon sailed out of a cloud with the wake of a
    spectral ship.
  I crouched and I crawled on my belly, my lariat coil
    looped wide.

Dimly and dark the mesas broke on the starry sky.
  A pall covered every color of their gorgeous glory at
    noon.
I smelt the yucca and mesquite, and stifled my heart's
    quick cry,
  And wormed and crawled on my belly to where he
    moved against the moon!

Some Moorish barb was that mustang's sire. His lines
    were beyond all wonder.
  From the prick of his ears to the flow of his tail he
    ached in my throat and eyes.
Steel and velvet grace! As the prophet says, God had
    "clothed his neck with thunder."
  Oh, marvelous with the drifting cloud he drifted across
    the skies!

And then I was near at hand—crouched, and balanced,
    and cast the coil;
  And the moon was smothered in cloud, and the rope
    through my hands with a rip!
But somehow I gripped and clung, with the blood in my
    brain aboil,—
  With a turn round the rugged tree-stump there on the
    purple canyon's lip.

Right into the stars he reared aloft, his red eye rolling
and raging.
He whirled and sunfished and lashed, and rocked the
earth to thunder and flame.
He squealed like a regular devil horse. I was haggard
and spent and aging—
Roped clean, but almost storming clear, his fury too
fierce to tame.

And I cursed myself for a tenderfoot moon-dazzled to
play the part,
But I was doubly desperate then, with the posse pulled
out from town,
Or I'd never have tried it. I only knew I must get a
mount and a start.
The filly had snapped her foreleg short. I had had to
shoot her down.

So there he struggled and strangled, and I snubbed him
around the tree.
Nearer, a little nearer—hoofs planted, and lolling
tongue—
Till a sudden slack pitched me backward. He reared
right on top of me.
Mother of God—that moment! He missed me . . .
and up I swung.

Somehow, gone daft completely and clawing a bunch of
his mane,
As he stumbled and tripped in the lariat, there I was—
up and astride.

And cursing for seven counties! And the mustang? *Just
insane!*
  Crack-bang! went the rope; we cannoned off the tree—
    then—gods, that ride!

A rocket—that's all, a rocket! I dug with my teeth and
nails.
  Why, we never hit even the high spots (though I
    hardly remember things),
But I heard a monstrous booming like a thunder of flap-
ping sails
  When he spread—well, *call* me a liar!—when he spread
    those wings, those wings!

So white that my eyes were blinded, thick-feathered and
wide unfurled
  They beat the air into billows. We sailed, and the
    earth was gone.
Canyon and desert and mesa withered below, with the
world.
  And then I knew that mustang; for I—was Bellero-
    phon!

Yes, glad as the Greek, and mounted on a horse of the
elder gods,
  With never a magic bridle or a fountain-mirror nigh!
My chaps and spurs and holster must have looked it?
  What's the odds?
  I'd a leg over lightning and thunder, careering across
    the sky!

And forever streaming before me, fanning my forehead
cool,
Flowed a mane of molten silver; and just before my
thighs
(As I gripped his velvet-muscled ribs, while I cursed myself for a fool),
The steady pulse of those pinions—their wonderful fall
and rise!

The bandanna I bought in Bowie blew loose and whipped
from my neck.
My shirt was stuck to my shoulders and ribboning out
behind.
The stars were dancing, wheeling and glancing, dipping
with smirk and beck.
The clouds were flowing, dusking and glowing. We
rode a roaring wind.

We soared through the silver starlight to knock at the
planets' gates.
New shimmering constellations came whirling into our
ken.
Red stars and green and golden swung out of the void
that waits
For man's great last adventure; the Signs took shape—
and then

I knew the lines of that Centaur the moment I saw him
come!
The musical-box of the heavens all around us rolled
to a tune

That tinkled and chimed and trilled with silver sounds
    that struck you dumb,
    As if some archangel were grinding out the music of
    the moon.

Melody-drunk on the Milky Way, as we swept and soared
    hilarious,
    Full in our pathway, sudden he stood—the Centaur of
    the Stars,
Flashing from head and hoofs and breast! I knew him
    for Sagittarius.
    He reared and bent and drew his bow. He crouched
    as a boxer spars.

Flung back on his haunches, weird he loomed—then leapt
    —and the dim void lightened.
    Old White Wings shied and swerved aside, and fled
    from the splendor-shod.
Through a flashing welter of worlds we charged. I knew
    why my horse was frightened.
    He *had* two faces—a dog's and a man's—that Baby-
    lonian god!

Also, he followed us real as fear. Ping! went an arrow
    past.
    My broncho buck-jumped, humping high. We plunged
    . . . I guess that's all!
I lay on the purple canyon's lip, when I opened my eyes
    at last—
    Stiff and sore and my head like a drum, but I broke no
    bones in the fall.

So you know—and now you may string me up. Such
   was the way you caught me.
  Thank you for letting me tell it straight, though you
   never could greatly care.
For I took a horse that wasn't mine! . . . But there's one
   the heavens brought me,
  And I'll hang right happy, because I know he is waiting for me up there.

From creamy muzzle to cannon-bone, by God, he's a
   peerless wonder!
  He is steel and velvet and furnace-fire, and death's su-
   premest prize;
And never again shall be roped on earth that neck that is
   "clothed with thunder" . . .
  String me up, Dave! Go dig my grave! *I rode him
  across the skies!*

                              William Rose Benét

EPISTLE TO BE LEFT IN THE EARTH

. . . It is colder now
                    there are many stars
                              we are drifting
North by the Great Bear
                    the leaves are falling
The water is stone in the scooped rocks
                              to southward
Red sun grey air
              the crows are

214

Slow on their crooked wings
                              the jays have left us
Long since we passed the flares of Orion
Each man believes in his heart he will die
Many have written last thoughts and last letters
None know if our deaths are now or forever
None know if this wandering earth will be found

We lie down and the snow covers our garments
I pray you
            you (if any open this writing)
Make in your mouths the words that were our names
I will tell you all we have learned
                                    I will tell you everything
The earth is round
                    there are springs under the orchards
The loam cuts with a blunt knife
                                    beware of
Elms in thunder
                  the lights in the sky are stars
We think they do not see
                          we think also
The trees do not know nor the leaves of the grasses
                                                      hear us
The birds too are ignorant
                            Do not listen
Do not stand at dark in the open windows
We before you have heard this
                                they are voices
They are not words at all but the wind rising
Also none among us has seen God
(. . . We have thought often

The flaws of sun in the late and driving weather
Pointed to one tree but it was not so)
As for the nights I warn you the nights are dangerous
The wind changes at night and the dreams come

It is very cold
               there are strange stars near Arcturus
Voices are crying an unknown name in the sky

Archibald MacLeish

LAMENT

Listen, children:
Your father is dead.
From his old coats
I'll make you little jackets;
I'll make you little trousers
From his old pants.
There'll be in his pockets
Things he used to put there,
Keys and pennies
Covered with tobacco;
Dan shall have the pennies
To save in his bank;
Anne shall have the keys
To make a pretty noise with.
Life must go on,
And the dead be forgotten;
Life must go on,
Though good men die;

216

Anne, eat your breakfast,
Dan, take your medicine,
Life must go on;
I forget just why.

Edna St. Vincent Millay

PARTING

Now I go, do not weep, woman—
Woman, do not weep;
Though I go from you to die,
We shall both lie down
At the foot of the hill, and sleep.

Now I go, do not weep, woman—
Woman, do not weep;
Earth is our mother and our tent the sky.
Though I go from you to die,
We shall both lie down
At the foot of the hill, and sleep.

Alice Corbin Henderson

PRAYER TO THE FATES

Clotho, Lachesis, and Atropos,
Stern trinity.
It is not much I ask,
Grant it, I pray.

O Clotho! drawing from the mist
The thread of life,
I pray you, sweep not wide your arm
In drawing mine, but let
The thread be brief.
Lachesis, at your web, hear me!
And weave my web
Firm, yet not tight, and let
The web be short but wide that men,
In speaking of me afterward, shall say:
"He lived!"
Atropos! Veiled divinity,
Fray not my web in cutting;
Cut it free, and straight.
Stern trinity, relentless three,
It is not much I ask,
Grant it, I pray.

Robert Louis Smith-Walker

SUNSET

Behold where Night clutches the cup of heaven
  And quaffs the beauty of the world away!
  Lo, his first draught is all of dazzling day;
The next he fills with the red wine of even
And drinks; then of the twilight's amber, seven
  Deep liquid hues, seven times, superb in ray,
  He fills—and drinks; the last, a mead pale-gray
Leaves the black beaker gemmed with starry levin.

218

Even so does Time quaff our mortality!
   First, of the effervescing blood and blush
Of virgin years, then of maturity
   The deeper glow, then of the pallid hush
Where only the eyes still glitter, till even they—
After a pause—melt in immenser day.

                              Percy MacKaye

TIME, YOU OLD GYPSY MAN

Time, you old gypsy man,
   Will you not stay,
Put up your caravan
   Just for one day?

All things I'll give you
Will you be my guest,
Bells for your jennet
Of silver the best.
Goldsmiths shall beat you
A great golden ring.
Peacocks shall bow to you,
Little boys sing.
Oh, and sweet girls will
Festoon you with may,
Time, you old gypsy,
Why hasten away?
Last week in Babylon,
Last night in Rome,
Morning, and in the crush

Under Paul's dome;
Under Paul's dial
You tighten your rein—
Only a moment,
And off once again;
Off to some city
Now blind in the womb,
Off to another
Ere that's in the tomb.

Time, you old gypsy man,
  Will you not stay,
Put up your caravan
  Just for one day?

Ralph Hodgson

BARE FEET

Savages
Not long ago
Felt their toes
Outspreading—so;

Liked the feeling
Of the cool
Pad in meadow,
Dip in pool.

Where their feet are
Yours will be—

Turned to earth and
Apple tree.

So to-day best
Run around
Barefoot on the
April ground.

Dorothy Aldis

PART EIGHT

QUESTIONS AND SUGGESTIONS

Crystal Moment

In plays, fiction, and narrative poetry, why do we like to see the line of action go up? How is this direction suggested by the word *climax*? Has this poem a climax? Should the climax be the ending?

Death and General Putnam

Does the rhythm in this poem fit the subject-matter?

What has the poet done with the repetitions? How do they help to build a mood?

To an Athlete Dying Young

What device makes the first two stanzas effective? Is it continued throughout the poem?

Do you notice a difference in style between stanzas 3, 6, and 7 on the one hand, and 4 and 5 on the other? Which style do you prefer? Which is more like that of the first two stanzas?

The Seed Shop

Of the contrasted pictures, which is most vivid to you? Would they have been vivid without the contrasts?

Richard Cory

What are the advantages of a "surprise ending"? Are there any disadvantages? The method is used again and again in humorous poetry; why not so often in serious poetry?

The Horse Thief

When a poet deliberately exaggerates throughout a poem, does he expect to be believed? What two main impressions is Benét trying to give the reader by use of the incredible?

Does the elaborateness of the detail make your imagination lazy, or stimulate it further?

Epistle to be Left in the Earth

Scientists do not agree how human life in general is most likely to come to an end. But suppose that the end did approach in the way that MacLeish fancies here. To bring before the reader the fear, the misery, the longing for life, the awe of the future, that would be in people's hearts, he has used a method very different from that seen in "The Horse Thief." What is it?

Lament

This brief masterpiece goes one step further than the preceding poem. In addition to the understatement, it is stripped bare of all that we think of as poetic and musical expression. Why is it so deliberately harsh and stark? What are the tremendous implications of the last line?

Parting

Alice Corbin Henderson has lived for years in the Southwest and made many translations and adaptations of Indian poetry. The figures of speech in it are always interesting. Here is an old Indian speaking to his squaw. To the very common idea of death as a sleep he adds the notion of a home to sleep in—what? How does he picture that home?

Prayer to the Fates

Figures of considerable length should be exact in detail. According to the classic conception of the three fatal spinners,

223

are their actions characteristic?   Are the processes correct?
Does each action build toward the climax?

Robert Louis Smith-Walker was a California boy who died
when he was nineteen. He wrote this at the age of eighteen.

Sunset

You can imagine, perhaps, how difficult it is for poets to
find original figures. Figures that have been used before—
as the one of the cup—must be varied. Here Night and Time
drink again and again of day and life. How does this varia-
tion make the figure more exact?

Notice that the picture is given first and then the comparison. What element of interest does that add?

Time, You Old Gypsy Man

A figure that serves as the background for a poem must
attract and hold attention. What two arresting ideas about
time are here developed by carrying out the figure in detail?
Do most of us feel interest in gypsies themselves, or in what
they symbolize?

Look back at Part Three to see whether any poem there
contains a figure that is carried through.

Bare Feet

How does the phrase "not long ago" echo the thought of the
preceding poem? Have you ever seen a time-chart of the ages
of human existence? Find one and see what it stresses.

Should you interpret the last stanza literally or symbolically?

PART EIGHT

SUGGESTED SUPPLEMENTARY READING

Older Poems

"Death, be not proud"	John Donne
A Vision	Henry Vaughan
We Are Seven	William Wordsworth
"When I have fears"	John Keats
The Indian Burying-Ground	Philip Freneau
Thanatopsis	William Cullen Bryant
Nature	Henry Wadsworth Longfellow
"After a hundred years"	Emily Dickinson
Evolution	John Bannister Tabb
The Wild Ride	Louise Imogen Guiney

Newer Poems

A Parting Guest	James Whitcomb Riley
Divers	Robert Haven Schauffler
Better Not to Know	Edith Lombard Squires
Story of a Life	Marion Strobel
Lucinda Matlock	Edgar Lee Masters
Omnia Exeunt in Mysterium	George Sterling
Cool Tombs	Carl Sandburg

Part Nine

*The web of our life is of a mingled yarn, good and
ill together.*

Shakespeare

FOREWORD

Stevenson once spoke of the "big empty words" that people use so freely. At certain times one realized, he said, that if one asked himself what he meant by fame, riches, or learning, the answer is far to seek. So we will not claim that the poems in this last section set forth "philosophies of life." But they have been arranged in such a way as to illustrate different attitudes toward four questions that we sometimes ask ourselves. From them you may get the desire to start on some very long and steep mental trails.

Also, they have been arranged to illustrate a little of what we mean when we talk about "poetic taste." Not so many years ago, the subjects that were considered fit for poetry were comparatively few; to-day poets deal with any aspects of life, quite often with ugly ones. Is this a step in the right direction? In the modern use of words and rhythms, too, there are tremendous variations from what have long been considered the norms of poetry. And what about brevity? Shall a poem be just long enough to "flash" its meaning, or shall it go into leisurely detail? Closely allied with the question of length is that of restraint (which was discussed in connection with Part Seven) *versus* fully-expressed emotion. Last, there is always the question of whether a poem should be direct enough in its expression to be perfectly clear at the first reading, or whether it should be rich in allusions, figures, or subtleties of diction, so that each rereading conveys new shades of meaning.

When people talk about "poetic taste," they all too often think only of their own preferences along these lines. Perhaps the following poems may show you some other criteria involved in this very complicated process of evaluating poetry.

FRENCH PEASANTS

These going home at dusk
    Along the lane,
After the day's warm work,
    Do not complain.

Were you to say to them,
    "What does it mean?
What is it all about,
    This troubled dream?"

They would not understand,
    They'd go their way,
Or, if they spoke at all,
    They'd surely say:

"Dawn is the time to rise,
    Days are to earn
Bread and the midday rest,
    Dusk to return;

"To be content, to pray.
    To hear songs sung,
Or to make wayside love,
    If one is young.

"All from the good God comes,
    All then is good;
Sorrow is known to Him,
    And understood."

229

One who had questioned all,
            And was not wise,
Might be ashamed to meet
            Their quiet eyes.

All is so clear to them,
            All is so plain;
These who go home at dusk,
            Along the lane.

Monk Gibbon

RENCONTRE

She walked to the music of her own mind's making,
The tall, spare spinster in the cheap, drab coat,
And her pale lips, faintly moving, their divine thirst were
        slaking
At the gods' own Hippocrene, where bright bubbles float.

As I passed her, in the half-light, on a waft of wind I
        caught the
Words once shaped by mortals beyond all mortal ken.
With Shelley and with Shakespeare she walked, with
        god-like Milton,
This poorest, palest, shabbiest of the daughters of men.

I looked at the girls, with their silken curls tossing,
Their redder lips than nature, their bright eyes of desire.
O brief is your springtime (I thought) my blossomy dar-
        lings,
But hers the authentic, the undying fire.

And I kissed the nearest blossom (was she Daphne? was
    she Chloe?)
And as betwixt my fingers her soft curls stirred
My thoughts were far from her, my thoughts were on
    the highway
Where walked the lone, gaunt spinster with the immor-
    tal word.

A. V. Stuart

WHO TRACK THE TRUTH

Quick and intangible as ever the quarry,
Now thought no more a phoenix of the air—
But now what murderous padding sublunary
Lithe thing, let them who track the truth declare.

They have come home, to die of eating and drinking.
They say it is useless, tracking hour by hour
What twists away into the wilds past thinking,
Or only turns to deafen and devour.

Yet these are they who in the night stole near it
When it would pause, and pant, and put behind
An instant its green eyes of desolate spirit,
Like jewels in the darkness of a mountain unmined.

And young men still, because indeed they are younger,
Lay down their girls and glasses—hoping at least
For a hero's life, or a death from thirst and hunger,
Or a bright look of the beast.

George Dillon

PRAYER

God, though this life is but a wraith,
   Although we know not what we use,
Although we grope with little faith,
   Give me the heart to fight—and lose.

Ever insurgent let me be,
   Make me more daring than devout;
From sleek contentment keep me free,
   And fill me with a buoyant doubt.

Open my eyes to visions girt
   With beauty, and with wonder lit—
But let me always see the dirt,
   And all that spawn and die in it.

Open my ears to music; let
   Me thrill with Spring's first flutes and drums—
But never let me dare forget
   The bitter ballads of the slums.

From compromise and things half-done,
   Keep me, with stern and stubborn pride;
And when, at last, the fight is won,
   God, keep me still unsatisfied.

Louis Untermeyer

BARTER

Life has loveliness to sell—
    All beautiful and splendid things,
Blue waves whitened on a cliff,
    Climbing fire that sways and sings,
And children's faces looking up
Holding wonder like a cup.

Life has loveliness to sell—
    Music like a curve of gold,
Scent of pine trees in the rain,
    Eyes that love you, arms that hold,
And for your spirit's still delight,
Holy thoughts that star the night.

Spend all you have for loveliness,
    Buy it and never count the cost,
For one white singing hour of peace
    Count many a year of strife well lost,
And for a breath of ecstasy
Give all you have been or could be.

                                        Sara Teasdale

THE GREAT LOVER

I have been so great a lover: filled my days
So proudly with the splendor of Love's praise,
The pain, the calm, and the astonishment,
Desire illimitable, and still content,

And all dear names men use, to cheat despair,
For the perplexed and viewless streams that bear
Our hearts at random down the dark of life.
Now, ere the unthinking silence on that strife
Steals down, I would cheat drowsy Death so far,
My night shall be remembered for a star
That outshone all the suns of all men's days.
Shall I not crown them with immortal praise
Whom I have loved, who have given me, dared with me
High secrets, and in darkness knelt to see
The inenarrable godhead of delight?
Love is a flame;—we have beaconed the world's night.
A city:—and we have built it, these and I.
An emperor:—we have taught the world to die.
So, for their sakes I loved, ere I go hence,
And the high cause of Love's magnificence,
And to keep loyalties young, I'll write those names
Golden forever, eagles, crying flames,
And set them as a banner, that men may know,
To dare the generations, burn, and blow
Out on the wind of Time, shining and streaming . . .
These I have loved:

              White plates and cups, clean-gleaming,
Ringed with blue lines; and feathery, faëry dust;
Wet roofs, beneath the lamp-light; the strong crust
Of friendly bread; and many tasting food;
Rainbows; and the blue bitter smoke of wood;
And radiant raindrops couching in cool flowers;
And flowers themselves, that sway through sunny hours,
Dreaming of moths that drink them under the moon;
Then, the cool kindliness of sheets, that soon

Smooth away trouble; and the rough male kiss
Of blankets; grainy wood; live hair that is
Shining and free; blue-massing clouds; the keen
Unpassioned beauty of a great machine;
The benison of hot water; furs to touch;
The good smell of old clothes; and other such—
The comfortable smell of friendly fingers,
Hair's fragrance, and the musty reek that lingers
About dead leaves and last year's ferns. . . .

                          Dear names,
And thousand other throng to me! Royal flames;
Sweet water's dimpling laugh from tap or spring;
Holes in the ground; and voices that do sing;
Voices in laughter, too; and body's pain,
Soon turned to peace; and the deep-panting train;
Firm sands; the dulling edge of foam
That browns and dwindles as the wave goes home;
And washen stones, gay for an hour; the cold
Graveness of iron; moist black earthen mold;
Sleep; and high places; footprints in the dew;
And oaks; and brown horse-chestnuts, glossy-new;
And new-peeled sticks; and shining pools on grass;—
All these have been my loves. And these shall pass,
Whatever passes not, in the great hour,
Nor all my passion, all my prayers, have power
To hold them with me through the gate of Death.
They'll play deserter, turn with the traitor breath,
Break the high bond we made, and sell Love's trust
And sacramental covenant to the dust.
—Oh, never a doubt but, somewhere, I shall wake,
And give what's left of love again, and make
New friends, now strangers. . . .

But the best I've known,
Stays here, and changes, breaks, grows old, is blown
About the winds of the world, and fades from brains
Of living men, and dies.
                    Nothing remains.

O dear my loves, O faithless, once again
This one last gift I give: that after men
Shall know, and later lovers, far-removed,
Praise you, "All these were lovely"; say, "He loved."

Mataiea, 1914.

Rupert Brooke

THE HEN AND THE ORIOLE

well boss did it
ever strike you that a
hen regrets it just as
much when they wring her
neck as an oriole but
nobody has any
sympathy for a hen because
she is not beautiful
while everyone gets
sentimental over the
oriole and says how
shocking to kill the
lovely thing this thought
comes to my mind
because of the earnest

endeavor of a
gentleman to squash me
yesterday afternoon when i
was riding up in the
elevator if i had been a
butterfly he would have
said how did that
beautiful thing happen to
find its way into
these grimy city streets do
not harm the splendid
creature but let it
fly back to its rural
haunts again beauty always
gets the best of
it be beautiful boss
a thing of beauty is a
joy forever
be handsome boss and let
who will be clever is
the sad advice
of your ugly little friend
                              archy

Don Marquis

EUCLID ALONE HAS LOOKED ON BEAUTY BARE

Euclid alone has looked on Beauty bare.
Let all who prate of Beauty hold their peace,
And lay them prone upon the earth and cease

To ponder on themselves, the while they stare
At nothing, intricately drawn nowhere
In shapes of shifting lineage; let geese
Gabble and hiss, but heroes seek release
From dusty bondage into luminous air.
O blinding hour, O holy, terrible day,
When first the shaft into his vision shone
Of light anatomized!   Euclid alone
Has looked on Beauty bare.   Fortunate they
Who, though once only and then but far away,
Have heard her massive sandal set on stone.

Edna St. Vincent Millay

THE EAGLE AND THE MOLE

Avoid the reeking herd,
Shun the polluted flock,
Live like that stoic bird,
The eagle of the rock.

The huddled warmth of crowds
Begets and fosters hate;
He keeps, above the clouds,
His cliff inviolate.

When flocks are folded warm,
And herds to shelter run,
He sails above the storm,
He stares into the sun.

238

If in the eagle's track
Your sinews cannot leap,
Avoid the lathered pack,
Turn from the steaming sheep.

If you would keep your soul
From spotted sight or sound,
Live like the velvet mole;
Go burrow underground.

And there hold intercourse
With roots of trees and stones,
With rivers at their source,
And disembodied bones.

Elinor Wylie

EMPIRE STATE TOWER

The far lands melt to orange and to grey.
The city lies, quiet but for a rumor,
A single voice. People are guessed. We hazard
The world we know is there, below, unseen.
And in the street the many beautiful
Unstaring walk unwaiting the knives of doom,
In sleep, or death, or love—the beautiful people
Setting up parapets against space and time,
Like this one where small contact is forgotten.

Pitiable remove, that we should ask to go
Away from earth, from the nudge of other minds;

Clumsy abstraction, that human beings forgo
For a short quiet the sight of their own kinds;
O strong unlove against our fellows here,
Never again set me so high, away
From action, pocketed in loneliness from fear,
And hurt, perhaps, but from the working-day.

Muriel Rukeyser

THE MAN WITH THE HOE

Written after seeing Millet's World-Famous Painting

God made man in His own image,
in the image of God made He him—
Genesis

Bowed by the weight of centuries he leans
Upon his hoe and gazes on the ground,
The emptiness of ages in his face,
And on his back the burden of the world.
Who made him dead to rapture and despair,
A thing that grieves not and that never hopes,
Stolid and stunned, a brother to the ox?
Who loosened and let down this brutal jaw?
Whose was the hand that slanted back this brow?
Whose breath blew out the light within this brain?

Is this the thing the Lord God made and gave
To have dominion over sea and land;
To trace the stars and search the heavens for power;
To feel the passion of Eternity?
Is this the Dream He dreamed who shaped the suns

And marked their ways upon the ancient deep?
Down all the stretch of Hell to its last gulf
There is no shape more terrible than this—
More tongued with censure of the world's blind greed—
More filled with signs and portents for the soul—
More fraught with danger to the universe.

What gulfs between him and the seraphim!
Slave of the wheel of labor, what to him
Are Plato and the swing of Pleiades?
What the long reaches of the peaks of song,
The rift of dawn, the reddening of the rose?
Through this dread shape the suffering ages look;
Time's tragedy is in that aching stoop;
Through this dread shape humanity betrayed,
Plundered, profaned and disinherited,
Cries protest to the Judges of the World,
A protest that is also prophecy.

O masters, lords and rulers in all lands,
Is this the handiwork you gave to God,
This monstrous thing distorted and soul-quenched?
How will you ever straighten up this shape;
Touch it again with immortality;
Give back the upward looking and the light;
Rebuild in it the music and the dream;
Make right the immemorial infamies,
Perfidious wrongs, immedicable woes?

O masters, lords and rulers in all lands,
How will the Future reckon with this Man?
How answer his brute question in that hour

When whirlwinds of rebellion shake the world?
How will it be with kingdoms and with kings—
With those who shaped him to the thing he is—
When this dumb Terror shall reply to God,
After the silence of the centuries?

Edwin Markham

"SCUM O' THE EARTH"

I

At the gate of the West I stand,
On the isle where the nations throng.
We call them "scum o' the earth";

Stay, are we doing you wrong,
Young fellow from Socrates' land?—
You, like a Hermes so lissome and strong
Fresh from the master Praxiteles' hand?
So you're of Spartan birth?
Descended, perhaps, from one of the band—
Deathless in story and song—
Who combed their long hair at Thermopylae's pass? . . .
Ah, I forget what straits (alas!),
More tragic than theirs, more compassion-worth,
Have doomed you to march in our "immigrant class"
Where you're nothing but "scum o' the earth."

II

You Pole with the child on your knee,
What dower brings you to the land of the free?

Hark! does she croon
The sad little tune
That Chopin once found on his Polish lea
And mounted in gold for you and for me?
Now a ragged young fiddler answers
In wild Czech melody
That Dvořák took whole from the dancers.
And the heavy faces bloom
In the wonderful Slavic way;
The little dull eyes, the brows a-gloom,
Suddenly, dawn like the day.
While watching these folk and their mystery,
I forget that we,
In our scornful mirth,
Brand them as "polacks"—and "scum o' the earth."

III

Genoese boy of the level brow,
Lad of the lustrous, dreamy eyes
Agaze at Manhattan's pinnacles now
In the first, sweet shock of a hushed surprise;
Within your far-rapt seer's eyes
I catch the glow of the wild surmise
That played on the *Santa Maria's* prow
In that still gray dawn,
Four centuries gone,
When a world from the wave began to rise.
Oh, who shall foretell what high emprise
Is the goal that gleams
When Italy's dreams
Spread wing and sweep into the skies?

243

Caesar dreamed him a world ruled well;
Dante dreamed Heaven out of Hell;
Angelo brought us there to dwell;
And you, are you of a different birth?—
You're only a "dago"—and "scum o' the earth"!

IV

Stay, are we doing you wrong
Calling you "scum o' the earth,"
Man of the sorrow-bowed head,
Of the features tender yet strong,—
Man of the eyes full of wisdom and mystery
Mingled with patience and dread?
Have not I known you in history,
Sorrow-bowed head?
Were you the poet-king, worth
Treasures of Ophir unpriced?
Were you the prophet, perchance, whose art
Foretold how the rabble would mock
That shepherd of spirits, ere long,
Who should gather the lambs to his heart
And tenderly feed his flock?
Man—lift that sorrow-bowed head. . . .
Behold, the face of the Christ!

The vision dies at its birth,
You're merely a butt of our mirth,
You're a "sheeny"—and therefore despised
And rejected as "scum o' the earth."

V

Countrymen, bend and invoke
Mercy for us blasphemers,
For that we spat on these marvellous folk,
Nations of darers and dreamers,
Scions of singers and seers,
Our peers, and more than our peers.
"Rabble and refuse," we name them
And "scum o' the earth," to shame them.
Mercy for us of the few, young years,
Of the culture so callow and crude,
Of the hands so grasping and rude,
The lips so ready for sneers
At the sons of our ancient more-than-peers.
Mercy for us who dare despise
Men in whose loins our Homer lies;
Mothers of men who shall bring to us
The glory of Titian, the grandeur of Huss;
Children in whose frail arms may rest
Prophets and singers and saints of the West.

Newcomers all from the eastern seas,
Help us incarnate dreams like these.
Forget, and forgive, that we did you wrong.
Help us to father a nation strong
In the comradeship of an equal birth
In the wealth of the richest bloods of earth.

Robert Haven Schauffler

COURAGE

Courage is but a word, and yet, of words,
The only sentinel of permanence;
The ruddy watch-fire of cold winter days,
We steal its comfort, lift our weary swords,
And on. For faith—without it—has no sense;
And love to wind of doubt and tremor sways;
And life forever quaking marsh must tread.

Laws give it not, before it prayer will blush,
Hope has it not, nor pride of being true.
'Tis the mysterious soul which never yields,
But hales us on and on to breast the rush
Of all the fortunes we shall happen through.
And when Death calls across his shadowy fields—
Dying, it answers: "Here! I am not dead!"

John Galsworthy

BIG BOY

Skirt turned you down
Because you worked in a steel mill?
Gave you the gate, laughed fit to kill?
Well, what do you expect?
You can't help that, big boy!

Burns on your eye,
On your arms, your chest, your hands?
Goin' to cry?

246

Them things an open hearth feller stands.
Damn, snap to, you, buck up!
Make the best of it, big boy!

Can't stand the work,
Back sore, shovel handle cuts like a knife?
How can you shirk?
You got to eat, ain't you, in this dirty life?
Hell, swing onto that hammer!
Put your back into it, big boy!

Hop on a freight,
Go some place where a man's got a chance?
That ain't your fate!
Weak head, strong back, and you got on pants.
Why, you're as dumb as me!
What else can you do, big boy?

Wish you could die,
Wish 'twas pneumonia 'stead of smoke makin' you
    coughin'?
Wish you could lie
Under the ground in a varnished pine coffin?
C——, you wish you was dead?
Huh! You ain't got nothin' on me, big boy!

John Beecher

THE CLIMBER

Out of a world whose beauty is desire,
A twisting flux where nothing is complete
And life's one hope is hope's eternal fire,

He strives with aching arms and weary feet.
Dizzied by time and the dark height before him,
Leaving behind him all his sires called light,
And heedless of the jeering age that bore him,
Alone he climbs into the starless night.
Almost a song whose echoes never ended,
Almost a picture telling all he meant,
Almost a poem ultimate and splendid,
Almost a love whose first dream never went:
Upward he yearns, heartsick and vision blurred,
To read in the black sky one finite word.

Carl Carmer

MOTHER TO SON

Well, son, I'll tell you:
Life for me ain't been no crystal stair.
It's had tacks in it,
And splinters,
And boards torn up,
And places with no carpet on the floor—
Bare.
But all the time
I'se been a-climbin' on,
And reachin' landin's,
And turnin' corners,
And sometimes goin' in the dark
Where there ain't been no light.
So, boy, don't you turn back.
Don't you set down on the steps

'Cause you finds it's kinder hard.
Don't you fall now—
For I'se still goin', honey,
I'se still climbin',
And life for me ain't been no crystal stair.

Langston Hughes

PART NINE

QUESTIONS AND SUGGESTIONS

French Peasants

Why is this purposely kept short and simple? Do you feel that it represents actuality? Does it make the lot of peasants seem enviable?

Rencontre

Notice that in this poem, as well as in "French Peasants," the picture is given through the eyes of an outsider. In which of the two poems does the outsider play a larger part in pointing the idea? In which does he seem more real? Why?

Do you like the meter that the poet uses?

Who Track the Truth

Why is truth called "murderous" as well as "quick" and "intangible"? Discuss in class whether you think you will remember the idea of the poem better for the elaborate comparison.

Hawthorne once said, "A man's bewilderment is the measure of his wisdom." Do you think it would make any difference whether he were of a scientific or an artistic temperament?

Prayer

After reading the poem aloud, what relation do you see between the idea and the form? Does the dominant personal tone lend vigor? What effective trick in wording runs throughout?

What would you say of the relation between man's power to think and man's happiness?

Barter

This is a very good example of the *lyric,* which has not been discussed as such before. Not only does it reveal the author's emotion, but it has the musical sound, in lines and words, that reminds us of the Greek custom of singing poetry to the accompaniment of a lyre. A good lyric should also convey to the reader something intangible, a certain color, mood, impression all its own. For thought takes second place when one is reading a lyric; it is the emotion that counts. Read the poem again with these criteria in mind.

The Great Lover

Although this poem reveals the author's emotion even more deeply than "Barter," we should not call it a pure lyric. Why not? Is it equally effective in conveying its idea? How does the idea go farther than that of "Barter"? Do you like having so many examples?

the hen and the oriole

"Archy" was a cockroach with literary leanings. When the office was deserted at night, he jumped from key to key of the typewriter till his poems were written. Of course he could not put in capitals or punctuation, because he could not press both shift and keys. Such was the device Don Marquis used to veil serious thoughts with flippancy. What new thought about beauty in human life is given by "your ugly little friend"? Do you object to classing this as poetry?

Euclid Alone Has Looked on Beauty Bare

By a large poetic jump from "Archy's" casual reflections we come to a formal sonnet in the strict Italian rhyme scheme. (See Reference List.) Why is it a most appropriate form for this particular poem?

It may help you to get this idea, which seems strange at first, to study some figure or group of figures in Greek sculpture, trying to see only lines, planes, proportions, and symmetry. Geometry depends on the conception of order. Does art?

The Eagle and the Mole

For what reasons might a man wish to tear himself clear of humanity? What would he gain from his isolation, as typified by the life of the eagle and the life of the mole?

What is the general tone of this poem? Is it a lyric?

Empire State Tower

In temporary isolation, what does the poet realize about the ties that bind her to humankind?

How does the sound of the poem suggest more warmth than the sound of "The Eagle and the Mole"?

The Man with the Hoe

Markham wrote this about a generation ago. Is his bitter arraignment of society for neglecting its responsibilities still true to-day?

Do you like long poems? What can they do that shorter ones cannot?

"Scum o' the Earth"

What is the meaning of the word "romantic" as it is applied to all art, including poetry? Apply the definition to this poem and see whether it fits.

Courage

One kind of courage enables people to meet sudden emergencies. What other kind is Galsworthy writing about? Which of these adjectives best describes the general tone of the poem: showy, stimulating, quiet, restrained, conventional, intense?

Big Boy

Not even the bitterest opponents of unconventional modern verse could deny that this poem has one thing characteristic of all real poetry. What? List three objections that might be made to it as poetry, and try to answer each.

Galsworthy says of courage, "Hope has it not." Which lines in "Big Boy" give the idea of hopelessness? To what extent are courage and hope related?

The Climber

What did Browning once write about a man's reach and his grasp?

Does this sonnet sound as formal as Miss Millay's? How does the rhyme-scheme differ? (See Reference List.) Difficult though the sonnet form is, it is tremendously popular among poets. Why?

Mother to Son

Is there any difference to your mind between courage and persistence? Notice that the figure used to express the latter idea is similar to the one in "The Climber." With what difference? How does the sound effect differ from that of "Big Boy"?

PART NINE

SUGGESTED SUPPLEMENTARY READING

Older Poems

Newer Poems

254

NOTES ON SOME ALLUSIONS IN THE POEMS

Part One

In a Certain Restaurant

Franz Hals (1581-1666) was a Dutch portrait-painter. Most of the men and women who sat for him belonged to the solid, comfortable, full-fed middle-class called burghers. (Notice the use of that word later in the poem.)

When Shakespeare Laughed

The *Mermaid Tavern,* favorite resort of London poets and playwrights in Shakespeare's day, is famous in our eyes because of its patrons; but doubtless the patrons themselves thought quite as much of the excellent food as of the company.

American Laughter

"*Artemus Ward*" was the pen-name of Charles Farrar Browne (1834-1867) who wrote of an imaginary traveling salesman of that name in a series of humorous books dealing with his adventures. He was one of Lincoln's favorite authors. Perhaps for that reason he has been remembered better than any other American humorist except Mark Twain (who, of course, wrote the tale of "The Jumping Frog of Calaveras County").

The Feet of the Young Men

In Kipling's day, the higher Himalayas were still unscaled, and even the lower slopes were only for the very daring. There native sportsmen and a few Englishmen hunted the fleet, shaggy-haired mountain goat called *Ovis Poli.*

255

Wishes for My Son

St. Cecilia is the patron saint of music and of the blind; her "day" is November twenty-second. She was a noble Roman matron who died a martyr for the Christian faith about 230. On the legend that she "praised God by instrumental and vocal music" many a picturesque story has been built up, and she has been the subject of famous paintings.

Part Two

The Riveter

In Greek myths, *Icarus* and his father, *Daedalus,* are represented as flying on wings fastened to their body by wax. (They were trying to escape from the wrath of the king of Crete.) Icarus flew too near the sun; the wax melted, his wings dropped from him, and he fell into the sea.

Part Three

The Barrel-Organ

Verdi lived from 1813 to 1901. He produced his first opera when he was twenty-five and his last when he was eighty. The best known, besides *Il Trovatore,* are *Rigoletto, La Traviata,* and *Aida.*

Kew Gardens, in a suburb of London, is the home of the Royal Botanic Gardens. The thousands of varieties of plants there make it one of the show places in southern England.

For some reason the part of the Thames River near Oxford is called the *Isis.* Although narrow, it is deep enough and straight enough to serve for Oxford crews' rowing. A towpath runs along its sides; spectators watch races from there and from moored houseboats that belong to various clubs and organizations.

The *City,* a part of downtown London, is the center of banking, insurance, and wholesale interests, as distinct from the shopping section.

256

The Saint

Joan of Arc lived from about 1412 to 1431. Cruelly betrayed in her lifetime, she was finally pronounced a saint by the Catholic Church. In connection with this poem, you should read Bernard Shaw's play, *Saint Joan*.

"Ecce ancilla Domini" is translated in the next line.

PART FOUR

Coast Cathedral

"Sursum Corda" is the Latin for "Lift up your hearts." This exhortation is made during the Roman Catholic service of the Mass and the Protestant Episcopal communion service. It is usually sung to very inspiring music by the choir.

PART FIVE

Dulce et Decorum Est

The full Latin phrase, quoted at the end of the poem, means "It is sweet and fitting to die for one's country."

PART SIX

In the Cliff Dwellings

> "And men lift grains and corn that in the bin
> Were stored while Age went out and Age came in,
> And figure over grinding stones, deep worn
> Before the Sphinx's face was flushed with morn."

These lives become more forceful if you realize that the statue of the *Sphinx* is about 4,700 years old. Traces of Indian culture in the Americas go back at least 5,000 years.

He Fell Among Thieves

Afghanistan touches the northwest border of India. The *Yassin River* is in the very northern tip, in the province of Kashmir. The struggle of the English with the fierce mountain tribesmen has continued up to this day.

The *Norman* period of architecture in England began with William's conquest, and developed gradually into the Gothic. It is solid, heavy, and richly decorated with geometric designs. Many large and small Norman churches in England are still in good condition. Of course they have been repaired during the years and sometimes they are only part of larger Gothic ones.

Park, as used in this poem, means part of a large private estate. Before the World War there were hundreds of estates in England consisting of 500-1,500 or more acres. They had been handed down in the same families, often from the Middle Ages.

Lepanto

This great sea-fight between the Christian League (Venice, the Papal States, Genoa, Spain) and the Turks was in 1571. Supreme Commander of the Christian galleys was *Don John of Austria*, half-brother of Philip II of Spain. The slaughter was terrific on both sides, but the Christian forces routed the Turks and freed thousands of Christian captives who had been forced to serve as rowers in the Turkish galleys. (It was the last sea-fight in which galleys were used.)

An equally thrilling account, though in prose, of another great sea battle between Christians and Saracens (717) may be found in *The Beauty of the Purple,* William Stearns Davis's novel about Leo III. Leo was a shepherd boy who rose through the army to become the head of Rome's Eastern empire.

The *cold queen of England* was Elizabeth; the *shadow of the Valois* was Charles IX of France, an invalid boy-king. England and France both had their hands too full at home to help in the East, and Spain's interests were divided between politics in Europe and her Western colonies (*evening isles fantastical*).

Mahound is an unusual name for Mohammed.

Azrael, Ariel, Ammon, were eastern divinities. Azrael was the angel of death.

St. Michael's Mount is at the tip of Cornwall (England). There is an old legend that the archangel Michael, who symbolizes righteous warfare, had sat in a natural chair on the seaward side of this huge rock.

Cervantes (1547-1616), known to all as the author of *Don Quixote,* had an extremely adventurous life as a fighter before he began to write. His left hand was permanently maimed by a wound received at Lepanto.

Cargoes

Nineveh, once the capital of the Assyrian Empire, was a center for much overland and oversea trade. It was situated in the midst of a rich country, and Sennacherib brought to it all the treasures he gained by conquest (8th century B.C.).

The region called *Ophir* was famous for its gold. No one knows exactly where it was—probably in Arabia, though perhaps in India or Zanzibar.

For Maister Geoffrey Chaucer

Petrarch (1304-1374) is usually thought of as the originator of the Renaissance movement in Italy. His enthusiasm for learning, especially that of the Greek and Latin civilizations, his interest in human achievements, and the high standard of literary art he set for his own poetry had much influence on his contemporaries and his successors. He perfected the sonnet as a poetic form. Most of his sonnets and lyrics were tributes to the charm of "Laura," an unidentified lady whom he adored for years.

Boccaccio (1313-1375) was an Italian prose writer of tremendous talent. Not a great scholar, he is nevertheless great because of his sympathetic understanding of all sorts of people and his skill in portraying their emotions. His *Decameron,* a collection of a hundred tales, may have given Chaucer the idea for *The Canterbury Tales*. In the latter years of his life, he became a great friend of Petrarch.

Sonnet

Caravels were much used for long voyages by the Spanish and Portuguese of Columbus's time. They were broad in the beam, low in the middle, and much raised at stern and bow. The term *forecastle* (shortened by sailors to *fo'c'sle*) is reminiscent of the "castle" at the bow of caravels.

PART SEVEN

The Look

Strephon, Colin, Chloe, Phyllis, Daphne, Amaryllis, Corydon, and *Thyrsis* are some of the more common names connected with *pastoral poetry*. That is a type which you really should know more about than can be given in a brief note here. Look up the term "pastoral" in some good encyclopedia, and then read the translations of the old pastorals given in *An Anthology of World Poetry* (Mark Van Doren) or some English pastoral lyrics of Shakespeare's time.

PART EIGHT

Death and General Putnam

The *Battle of Bunker Hill* (near Boston) was the first major one of the American Revolution (June 17, 1775). School children living in Boston are still given a holiday on its anniversary.

The Horse Thief

Bellerophon rode the winged horse *Pegasus,* according to a very ancient Greek myth. In fact, the myth is so old that some scholars say its hero was Asiatic, rather than Greek.

That idea would make it more akin to the second myth used in the poem. *Sagittarius,* the Archer or the Centaur on older charts, is one of the signs of the Zodiac, and the Zodiac was a conception of the ancient Babylonians. They divided the heavens into twelve belts, or "signs," corresponding to the constellations in the belts through which the sun passed at different times of the year. The device has always been used by astrologers.

Prayer to the Fates

Just a word of caution: Do not confuse these three Fates of Greek mythology with the three Furies (the horrible creatures with whips of snakes who tormented sinners) or with Nemesis, whom the Greeks thought of as personifying the wrath of the gods at wrongdoing. Mightier than any of these was the dread avenger of sin, Ate.

The whole idea of fate is the keystone of Greek tragedy.

Time, You Old Gypsy Man

Paul's dome and *Paul's dial* refer to the imposing cathedral of Saint Paul's, which is in a very busy downtown section of London.

PART NINE

Rencontre

The word *Hippocrene* is interesting in connection with the myth of Pegasus. A spring on a mountain in Greece sacred to the Muses and Apollo was supposed to have been formed by the stamping of the winged horse's hoof. Hence it was named Hippocrene, the "fountain of the horse."

For *Daphne* and *Chloe,* see the note on "The Look."

Euclid Alone Has Looked on Beauty Bare

If everyone in school took geometry, everyone would know who *Euclid* was. But at that, everyone might not know when he lived. He taught and founded a school at Alexandria about 300 B.C.

"Scum o' the Earth"

It is to be hoped you already know that the Greek philosopher *Plato* (428-348 B.C.) was one of the mightiest minds in all world history. Lately some high-school students have been studying his dialogue called *The Republic* because the different theories of government it sets forth are all more or less exemplified in different countries to-day.

In the work of *Praxiteles* (about 350 B.C.), one of the later Greek sculptors, we see a tendency away from dignity and toward humanity—something of the same interest in mankind as appears in the tragedies of Euripides, who, however, lived a century earlier.

Dante Alighieri (1265-1321) is still regarded as the greatest of Italian poets. It would be almost as presumptuous to try to deal with his work in this brief space as with Plato's. Perhaps you have read part of *The Divine Comedy*. If you have, you know why people call him great. His work was not appreciated until after his death, probably on account of his being exiled from Italy for his political views.

Michelangelo (1475-1564) has been called the most famous sculptor of the Italian Renaissance. His figures are large and grand; the ones of Moses and of David are the best known. He also performed a gigantic feat in painting the ceiling of the Sistine Chapel in Rome. It took him four and a half years.

POETS AS PEOPLE

Lord Dunsany once wrote a short play about the disillusionment of a poet who for years had worshipped Fame as a remote, exquisite goddess but found her, when she finally came to him, a vulgar creature who bawled out of the window to the crowd below that he ate bacon and eggs for breakfast. The degree to which artists of any sort resent having the details of their lives bared varies considerably; some poets, for instance, are very reserved, while others are frankly exhibitionists. Most of them, however, would probably agree that it was their work they wanted to have remembered rather than their personal history or characteristics.

The poet is "a man speaking to men," as Wordsworth put it, and generally leads a life not very different outwardly from that of the average intelligent person. The great difference lies in what he gets out of it inwardly. From the preceding poems you have seen some of the unusual and beautiful interpretations that poets can give to the common experiences of life. Now, to emphasize the point that poets are not strange creatures with "flashing eyes and floating hair," follows a section of what you might call collective biography. In it certain things common to the interests of all of us are illustrated by allusions to the lives of some poets whose work you have seen represented.

Some have found inspiration at home, while others have obeyed the wanderlust. More than half of the Americans have at some time traveled or lived in Europe, and longer trips are not uncommon. MacLeish has journeyed as far as

Persia. Sara Teasdale was fascinated by the Near East and Greece; Dillon also saw Greece when he was traveling on a Guggenheim fellowship. Amelia Josephine Burr spent two years going around the world. Eunice Tietjens and her husband, whenever the fancy strikes them, pack up and set off for places as remote as China and Tunisia. Hughes spent several years on the west coast of Africa; recently he has lived in Mexico. Johnson was United States consul to Venezuela and Nicaragua. Our Pacific possessions have interested three poets: Sandburg visited in Hawaii, Snow traveled widely in Alaska, and Agnes Kendrick Gray lived several years in the Philippines. The British poets, of course, think nothing of trips across the Atlantic, and a good many of them have been to the United States on lecture tours—Drinkwater, Gibson, Masefield, Nichols, Sassoon, Stephens, Yeats—or have lived here temporarily. Kipling built a house in Vermont which was his home till prying curiosity made him miserable; Noyes taught at Princeton University for seven years; Galsworthy wrote two novels while he was basking in the sun of Arizona and California. Brooke crossed the United States on his way to Tahiti. Nichols taught English literature at the Imperial University in Tokyo. Three Canadian poets—Cicely Fox Smith, Service, and Stringer—have seen most of the world between them. Turner was born in the farthest land, Australia. Masefield probably holds the record for the number of knots he has sailed at sea and the strange ports his ships have touched.

Of interest to Americans is the fact that some of our poets have "adopted" very different parts of the country from the ones where they were born. We find Mid-Westerners who now live in the East or in the Southwest, Easterners who have gone to the South, Far-Westerners and Southerners who have chosen the East. The largest class of American poets represented in this volume are those from the Middle Atlantic

States; the Mid-Western group are a very close second, the New Englanders third, and the rest scattered. As a whole, the poetry has a general American flavor rather than a local flavor, although some poets have identified their work closely with that part of the country in which they live—Frost, Dresbach, Sarett, Jeffers.

Social backgrounds also vary widely. They are important because nowadays poetry is dealing more and more with the conditions and problems of modern living, and any poet's attitude toward those is bound to be influenced by his upbringing and activities. In the early environments of American poets, one finds everything from luxurious family mansions to slum streets. Education was thus a matter of course to some, and to others a prize to be struggled for. By whatever roads they followed, the great majority secured college degrees or their equivalent in private study. Three of the men— Coffin, Engle, and Morley—were Rhodes scholars at Oxford. Jeffers and Eunice Tietjens were schooled abroad till their twenties. Daly and Marquis became newspaper men while young; Untermeyer, after finishing high school, went into the family jewelry business; Lindsay attended art school. Nine of them left college or their post-college occupations to enter the World War—Benét, Carmer, Coffin, Cummings, Dresbach, Hillyer, MacLeish, Schauffler, and Snow. All of them were fortunate enough to return. Not so with their brother-poets across the sea. Brooke, Owen, Sorley, and Thomas lost their lives, Owen only a week before the Armistice. Gibson, Nichols, Sassoon, and Service were all wounded. The World War, by the way, has been the second strongest influence on English poetry of this century. Strongest of all, however, has been the old one—love of the countryside. That has been an anodyne alike to those who knew and loved it as children and to the few who came to it later in life, like Davies and Gibson, after having known the seamy side of cities and towns. English poets have been more occupied with serving their government than American ones have; five of them—Hardy, Newbolt, Noyes, Squire, and Wolfe—have won knighthood or orders of merit. In connection with this point, we might consider four Irish poets separately. Rebels from English domination, they were actuated by patriotism even more intense. MacDonagh was executed for his part in the "Easter week" uprising. "A.E." (George W. Russell) spent years trying to improve agricultural conditions in Ireland. Yeats led the way in the revival of the ancient Gaelic culture, and Stephens has followed in his footsteps. But Lysaght, an Irish landowner, is pro-English, and Strong has lived in England since he was young. Most English poets belong to the middle class of society and have had the traditional classical education, which has made them rather conservative in their views. Recently, however, a group of young Oxford graduates headed by Auden (whose work is not represented here) and Spender have been propounding extreme measures for social reform.

All of us, at some time or other, have had a "push" from some force that has entered our lives—other people, books, trips we may have taken to strange places, and so forth. A few of the more dramatic influences in the lives of our poets have been as follows. Cullen attributes the beginning of his serious interest in poetry to the publication in his high-school magazine of a poem he had written for an English assignment. Two early memories have colored all of Sarett's work —one of the piny shores of Lake Superior, the other of Chicago slums. Alice Corbin Henderson's many translations and adaptations of Navajo poetry are the result of a trip to Arizona. Weaver might never have written his poems "in American" if he and a group of his friends had not read and argued about *The American Language,* by H. L. Mencken. Yeats' interest in Ireland's past dates from the days when he sat around turf fires listening to tales told by Connaught peasants.

The shock of her first contact with brutal realities at the time of the Sacco-Vanzetti case changed the entire tone of Edna St. Vincent Millay's poetry. A striking example of poetic debt is that which Thomas owed to Frost. They met while Frost was spending two years in England, before the War. Thomas was thirty-six; he had written twenty-five volumes of fiction and other prose, but never any poetry. But thanks to inspiration received from Frost he began to write poetry—very good poetry, too—and wrote nothing else during the three years before he was killed at Arras.

Great differences are to be found in the amounts of poetry produced by individual writers and in the other types of literature at which they try their skill. The three most versatile authors represented here, all writing at least three types equally well, are Kipling, Chesterton, and Galsworthy. With the two latter, we must admit, poetry was a side line; but each wrote some poems that will always be remembered. Counting poetry only, the most prolific are Jeffers, Lindsay, Amy Lowell, E. A. Robinson, Sandburg, Untermeyer, Gibson, Masefield, Newbolt, and Noyes. Others, besides a fair amount of poetry, have written volumes of at least one kind of prose, or else drama. Most of you probably know Drinkwater's *Abraham Lincoln,* MacKaye's *The Canterbury Pilgrims,* Marquis's *The Old Soak,* MacLeish's *The Fall of the City* and *Panic* (for radio). Dozens more stand to the credit of poets. The five who are probably best known to you as writers of fiction are Masters, Margaret Widdemer, Hardy, Stringer, and Strong; as writers of non-fictional prose, Carmer, Kreymborg, Morley, Untermeyer, and Davies. Three women—Dorothy Aldis, Eunice Tietjens, and Cicely Fox Smith—have written delightful children's books. Weaver adapted for the screen that classic for the young in heart of all ages, *Tom Sawyer.* A few poets write very little, lavishing a great deal of time and care on each slim volume. This method, although it may not suit the modern tempo, sometimes produces beautiful results; witness A. E. Housman.

In the *Foreword,* it was pointed out that poetry is usually good in proportion to the intensity of feeling that produces it. Naturally, poets cannot live all the time at the peak of inspiration; so most of them have found other occupations to fill their time, and incidentally to earn money, while poetic inspiration rests. A full catalogue of their avocations would be much too long. But here are some that indicate the diversity of interests and abilities. Auslander makes translations from French, German, and Italian. Burnet, Daly, Marquis, and Morton are or were newspaper men or columnists. Dillon used to write advertising copy; he is now editor of *Poetry,* the oldest and best-known magazine of its type in America. Hooker does librettos for operas. Sarett was for years a forest ranger and still spends several months yearly in the woods alone or with his Indian friends. Kreymborg and his wife run puppet shows. Eaton is much interested in Boy Scout work; he also has a full-time job teaching playwriting at Yale. Stringer used to run a huge farm in Canada. Turner's life is very much bound up with music, especially for the organ. Lecturing is a popular sport with poets, and many of them are in great demand. Some of them make surprisingly good teachers in all sorts of formal and informal positions. Hortense Flexner's job must be interesting: she is manager of a girls' club formed by the Curtis Publishing Company to promote writing. The great majority of poets, both women and men, are married and have children.

Their hobbies are legion. If you wanted to know about modern art, Cummings could tell you a great deal and show you his book *CIOPW,* consisting of work done in charcoal, ink, oil, pencil, and water color. Marquis was interested almost equally in art and in the theater. MacKaye has done extensive folk research among the Kentucky mountaineers.

Sandburg has collected folk songs and tunes in use among all classes of American laborers and tramps; you ought to hear him sing some of them to his guitar, but if you can't, read *An American Songbag.* Muriel Rukeyser learned flying at the Roosevelt School of the Air. E. A. Robinson and Chesterton used to devour detective yarns. Schauffler won matches for America on the tennis team in the Olympic games at Athens. Snow is happiest when spending summers on the coast of Maine, fishing and talking to fisher folk. Elinor Wylie was fond of collecting books, china, and bird prints. Amy Lowell had two passions: gardens, and all-night conversations with a group of congenial friends. Auslander, after Amy Lowell's death, wrote a series of sonnets one of which portrays a scene of this sort at her beautiful home—a picture complete even to the clouds of smoke from the big black cigars that she invariably puffed away at as she talked. English poets, by the way, all delight in conversation. Strong is much interested in dialects; like the professor in *Pygmalion,* he could probably tell locality from any English or Irish speech. Drinkwater had a fine stamp collection. Sassoon has been a great fox-hunting man. Noyes rowed for Oxford in his university days, and still loves water-sports so much that he has made his home on the Isle of Wight. Honors in hobbies, perhaps, should go to Masefield, for his has benefited other people as well as himself. He inaugurated and popularized the yearly Verse-Speaking Festivals, which have built up a love for poetry in many people who had never before heard it read aloud finely. We need more of that sort of thing over here.

Where can you find out more, yourselves, about those seventy-six interesting people and about the other thirty in the collection whose names have not been mentioned here? Sources of information are reference books such as *Who's Who, Who's Who in America, Living Authors,* and many others; brief biographies found in various anthologies and volumes of modern poetry; magazine articles and newspaper articles, which can be located through *The New York Times Index, The Magazine Index,* and the *International Index.* If you will glance over a good Sunday supplement each week and the little magazine *Poetry* every month, you will keep fairly up to date. Whenever you come across the latest pictures of poets, cut them out for a scrapbook. If you are genuinely interested in any one poet and unable to find out anything about him or her from the usual sources of information, it is always possible to write to the publishers of magazines or books and the editors of anthologies (in care of the publishers) to ask for the poet's address. But do not make a practice of that, for publishers, editors, and poets are busy people. Moreover, it will really give you more satisfaction in the end to track down information yourselves through some ingenious detective work.

Anyway, as was said at first, a poet's writings are far more significant than the details of his life. So read other poems in poets' published volumes and watch for new ones. Remember, too, that there are many other modern poets whom you will enjoy as you grow older, and that there are young ones who are constantly forging to the front. Interest in modern poetry cannot be static. It goes forever forward.

REFERENCE LIST OF TECHNICAL TERMS

I

THE MOVEMENT OF POEMS

1. *Rhythm*

This word comes from a Greek verb meaning "to flow"; so first we ought to get from it the idea of continuous movement. Rhythms of different kinds are to be found in every human activity, in the sounds of nature, and in all the arts. In poetry, rhythms are large underlying patterns in sound, whereas meters are smaller surface patterns in sound. Both rhythm and meter require the combination of accented and unaccented syllables in successive words. But we usually think of meter as a measure for individual lines, and of rhythm as the movement that flows through the entire poem. Why is that different from the metrical movement of all the lines together? That is difficult to say. The difference may be due to the effect produced by (1) various kinds and positions of metrical irregularities; (2) varied intervals between pauses in sense that runs through line-groups or stanzas; or (3) the arrangement of heavy or light voice-stresses on certain sounds. It is due also to something that defies analysis but wins response, the part played by movement in conveying mood. Rhythm is one reason why two poems written in the same meter will give entirely dissimilar impressions when read aloud. Make the experiment with "Coast Cathedral" and "The Seed Shop." If your class has time at the end of your poetry unit, it might be fun to examine a few poems for the contribution of (1), (2), and (3) to their rhythm. Do not be discouraged if you cannot get very far in a day's discussion. Whole volumes have been written on rhythm.

2. *Meter*

Meter has already been defined as the combination of accented and unaccented syllables within individual lines. It follows various schemes in the number of accents and in the kind of feet employed.

3. *Accent*

Accent, or stress as it is sometimes called, occurs when the voice of the reader hits certain syllables harder than it does others. Two things about accent should be remembered: (1) normal accents and foot accents should correspond when possible; (2) accents on important words should be made heavier than those on unimportant words or parts of words.

4. *Names of Lines According to Accent*

    a. A line with only one accent is called *monometer*. See "Plan for a Summer Day."

    b. A line with two accents is called *dimeter*. See "Bare Feet."

    c. A line with three accents is called *trimeter*. See "The Ancient Beautiful Things."

    d. A line with four accents is called *tetrameter*. See "Wild Strawberries."

    e. A line with five accents is called *pentameter*. See "Richard Cory."

    f. A line with six accents is called *hexameter*. See "Bill's Grave."

    g. A line with seven accents is called *heptameter*. See "Hastings Mill."

    h. A line with eight accents is called *octometer*. See "The Feet of the Young Men."

5. *Foot*

A foot consists of one accented syllable and one or more unaccented syllables. In modern poetry, for some particular effect, the number of syllables in a foot may be as many as four or even five. Both older and modern poets use the one-syllable foot freely when that syllable is heavily accented. But normally, a foot will contain either two or three syllables.

6. *Feet That Give Their Names to Lines*

a. *Iambus*

The iambus is the most common foot in English poetry. It consists of an unaccented syllable followed by an accented one. It is most often used in lines with three, four, or five accents.

For *iambic trimeter,* see "The Shepherd to the Poet."

For *iambic tetrameter,* see "Leisure."

For *iambic pentameter,* see "Counter-Attack."

b. *Trochee*

The trochee is the opposite of the iambus. It consists of an accented syllable followed by an unaccented one. Very often, in a trochaic line, only the accented syllable of the last foot is given.

See "To the Thawing Wind."

c. *Anapaest*

The anapaest consists of two unaccented syllables followed by an accented one. It is most commonly used in lines with four accents. The first foot in an otherwise anapaestic line is often iambic.

See "American Laughter."

d. *Dactyl*

The dactyl is the opposite of the anapaest. It consists of an accented syllable followed by two unaccented ones. It is an uncommon foot in English poetry; when used, it occurs chiefly in lines of two or six accents. (Dactylic hexameter was the meter of the Greek and Latin epics.) See "Time, You Old Gypsy Man."

7. *Scansion*

Scansion is an artificial but sometimes useful method of indicating the kind of feet in a line of poetry (by using ´ for an accented syllable and ˘ for an unaccented), / / for the divisions between feet, and for pauses in the sense // (between words). A line of scansion without words might look like this:

˘ ´ / ˘ ´ / ˘ ´ / ˘ // ´ / ˘ ´ /

or with words

The Kings / are pass / ing death / ward; // let / them be. /

What meter is that?

Scansion shows very clearly what feet in a line are irregular, i.e., do not follow the pattern of the prevailing number of feet. (The subject of irregularities is much too long to take up here, but fascinating. They give life and interest to lines.)

8. *Caesura*

Caesura was the Latin name for the pause within a line that is necessitated by the sense. There may be more than one pause within a line, or none at all.

9. *Kinds of Lines*

    a. An *end-stopped* line is one in which a sense group of words is completed at the end of a line (usually with punctuation).

       See "The Unseen."

    b. A *run-on* line is one in which the grammatical or logical sense is carried over to another line. (Note: This

274

trick is a very important one to master if you are writing blank verse.)

See "Reproof to Death."

c. A *masculine* line is one which ends with the accented word in a complete foot. It occurs only when lines are iambic or anapaestic.

See "Song" and "An Open Boat."

d. A *feminine* line is one which has an extra unaccented syllable at the end. This also occurs only in iambic or anapaestic lines.

See "Death and General Putnam" (refrain line) and "An Open Boat."

e. A *truncated* (cut-off) line is one which omits one or two unaccented syllables of the last foot. It is found in trochaic or dactylic lines (very commonly in trochaic).

See "The Look" and "Anthony Crundle."

II

THE GROUPING OF LINES IN POETRY

1. The word "verse" is often incorrectly used to denote a rhyming group of lines. Properly speaking, it is applied to one line of poetry (a verse) or to kinds of poetry (modern verse) or to poetry in general, usually to denote an inferior kind of poetry.

2. *Blank verse,* the commonest of all English meters, is unrhymed iambic pentameter. It is a very flexible meter, lending itself equally well to all degrees of formality and informality. It has been used for four hundred years.

See "The Man with the Hoe" and "The Code."

3. *Verse paragraphs* are irregular divisions of blank verse or couplets according to sense.

See the same two poems.

4. A *stanza* is a group of rhyming lines. Such a group

should not be called a verse. Several stanzas constitute a poem.

    a. The *couplet* is the simplest form of stanza, consisting of two rhyming lines.

        See "Man and Dog."

    b. *Heroic couplet* is the name that has been given since 1660 to a particular kind of couplet, iambic pentameter. It was the form Chaucer had used almost three hundred years before that, although in his hands it had more pleasing irregularities than were used by 17th and 18th century writers. The tendency of any couplet is toward monotony. Why?

        See "For Maister Geoffrey Chaucer."

    c. The *quatrain* is the most common form of stanza. The metrical combinations used are many, and there are five effective ways of rhyming the lines. (See Designation of Rhyme.)

    d. The *ballad stanza,* a form of the quatrain, has been a very popular form for the last six or seven hundred years in narrative poetry. The orthodox form has iambic tetrameter in the first and third lines and iambic trimeter in the second and fourth. The second and fourth always rhyme, whether the others do or not.

        Look over some collection of old English and Scottish ballads.

  5. *Refrains* are lines which are repeated for effect at fairly regular intervals through a poem. They usually come at the end of stanzas six lines or more in length. The repetitions may be exact, or slightly varied.

See "The Feet of the Young Men" and "General William Booth."

  6. The *rondeau* is a form borrowed from French poetry. It has fifteen lines, thirteen of them iambic tetrameter in which only two rhyming sounds are employed, and two of them, a

refrain, iambic dimeter, unrhyming. The first words of the poem and the dimeter lines must be the same.

See "When Shakespeare Laughed."

7. The *sonnet* is a poem of fourteen iambic pentameter lines developing a complete thought, different aspects of which are shown in the first eight lines (*octave*) and the last six (*sestet*). The form is almost as popular as it is difficult. Two schemes of rhyming are usually considered the most correct, although many poets deviate slightly from them. A comparison of the two sonnets below will show the difference. The first one is called Italian because Petrarch used the rhyme scheme six hundred years ago; the second, Shakespearean or Elizabethan.

NATURE

As a fond mother, when the day is o'er,	a
Leads by the hand her little child to bed,	b
Half willing, half reluctant to be led,	b
And leave his broken playthings on the floor,	a
Still gazing at them through the open door,	a
Nor wholly reassured and comforted	b
By promises of others in their stead,	b
Which, though more splendid, may not please him more;	a
So Nature deals with us, and takes away	c
Our playthings one by one, and by the hand	d
Leads us to rest so gently, that we go	e
Scarce knowing if we wish to go or stay,	c
Being too full of sleep to understand	d
How far the unknown transcends the what we know.	e

Henry Wadsworth Longfellow

Since there's no help, come let us kiss and part—	a
Nay, I have done, you get no more of me;	b
And I am glad, yea, glad with all my heart,	a
That thus so cleanly I myself can free;	b
Shake hands for ever, cancel all our vows	c
And when we meet at any time again,	d
Be it not seen in either of our brows	c
That we one jot of former love retain.	d
Now at the last gasp of love's latest breath,	e
When, his pulse failing, passion speechless lies,	f
When faith is kneeling by his bed of death,	e
And innocence is closing up his eyes,	f
—Now if thou would'st, when all have given him over,	g
From death to life, thou might'st him yet recover!	g

M. Drayton

For an explanation of the letters at the right of the lines turn to Designation of Rhyme, unless you can figure them out for yourself.

8. *Fixed Forms*. The *rondeau* is the only one of the *fixed forms* borrowed from the French of which there is an example in this book. There are six others, all difficult; the only one of these which you need to remember anything about is the *ballade*. Do not confuse that with the English *ballad;* it is absolutely different. A good example of it which you may know is the one that Cyrano de Bergerac composed while he was dueling with Valvert.

9. *Unconventional Forms.*

  a. *Free verse* (or *cadenced verse*)

  The last twenty-five years have witnessed an astonishing growth of a kind of poetry that can be like the little

278

girl with the curl. Its chief originator in America was Amy Lowell, who was a real scholar and a painstaking craftsman. Her studies of cadenced verse in French had shown her the difficulty of writing it well in English, and she tried to make people see what principles govern it. Here are a few.

Cadence is the rhythmical flow of sound caused by the rising and falling of a reader's voice between the drawings of breath. The fall should correspond to a pause in the flow of the idea.

Cadenced verse is non-syllabic; it is based upon accents. If there are many syllables between accents, the voice hurries over them; if few, it lingers. Thus variety of sound is created. There is no regular meter.

(There are no regular rhymes in cadenced verse; but subtle and beautiful effects may be gained by rhyme sounds placed irregularly.)

Cadenced verse is not divided into regular stanzas, but it has divisions, depending on completeness of rhythm and thought. The idea of completeness suggests a circle; hence free-verse writers call these divisions *strophes,* a term borrowed from the Greek. (The chorus in Greek tragedy always made a "strophe" or circuit around the central altar, chanting meanwhile.) Some thought or sound at the end of each strophe should bring one back to a thought or sound at the beginning.

It is not easy to make cadences pleasant, accents varied, and line-groups satisfyingly complete. But it looks easy. That is why so many would-be poets joyfully plunged into this new form without knowing or caring about these laws or others that might be given here if there were time. To them it was merely the throwing off of the shackles of rhyme and meter. The results were either absurd or tragic. The few poets who have taken it seriously have produced fine things; a very few, like Sandburg and Jeffers, have adapted the form to their own style.

The only real test of whether a piece of "free" verse is good or not is to read it aloud many times.

In this collection there are eighteen poems in free verse. Try to pick them out. If you have time in class, discuss them as a group.

b. *Polyphonic prose*

Amy Lowell and John Gould Fletcher went one step further, to a form which looks like prose, but is far from it. To quote Miss Lowell:

"It is printed in that manner for convenience, as it changes its character so often, with every wave of emotion, in fact. The word 'polyphonic' is its keynote. 'Polyphonic' means 'many-voiced' and the form is so called because it makes use of all the 'voices' of poetry, that is: meter, *vers libre,* assonance, alliteration, rhyme, and return. It employs every form of rhythm, even prose rhythm at times, but usually holds no particular one for long. It is an exceedingly difficult form to write, as so much depends upon the poet's taste. The rhymes may come at the ends of the cadences, or may appear in close juxtaposition to each other, or may be only distantly related. It is an excellent medium for dramatic portrayal, for stories in scenes, as it permits of great vividness of presentation."

See "The Bombardment."

WORD-SOUNDS IN POEMS

1. *Rhyme*

By rhyme we mean the correspondence in sound between the last accented syllable of one line and the last accented syllable of another. The consonants preceding the vowel in the last syllable must be different, but the vowel and the last consonant or consonants are the same.

a. Designation of rhyme, for convenience' sake, is usually made by the first letters of the alphabet; *a* stands for the rhyming sound of the first line and of any other lines in which that sound occurs, *b* for the rhyming sound of the first *different* line and of any other lines in which that sound occurs, and so on. See II, 7, *sonnet.*

b. *Single rhyme* occurs when the last accents of lines fall on the last syllables of words corresponding in sound.

c. *Double rhyme* occurs when the last accents of the lines fall on the next-to-last syllables of words corresponding in sound.

d. *Triple rhyme* (rare and always comic in effect) carries the accent and rhyme back one syllable further; for example, Browning says of the Mayor of Hamelin,

". . . his paunch grew mutinous
For a plate of turtle, green and glutinous."

e. *Internal rhyme* is a correspondence in sound between the word at the end of a line and a word near the middle. See the dance song in "The Barrel-Organ."

2. *Assonance*

Assonance is the correspondence of vowel-sounds in words where the consonants before and after the vowels may be different. Recent poets have made considerable use of assonance in final syllables as a substitute for rhyme.

See "The Ancient Beautiful Things."
Assonance is also used within lines.
See "Lepanto."

3. *Alliteration*

By alliteration we mean repetition of the same consonants within different words in a line or group of lines. There is no word-device more effective than alliteration when it is good and none more cheap when it is overdone.

See "The Kings Are Passing Deathward."

4. *Repetition*

Repetition of words should be planned for effect. Sometimes they emphasize an idea, as "scum o' the earth," and again they give definite sounds that tie the tone-pattern together, as the words "laughed" and "laughter" do in "American Laughter." "Boom," as used in "The Bombardment," serves both purposes. Repetitions of phrase need not always have each word exactly alike, so long as the important ones are the same.

5. *Onomatopoeia*

Onomatopoeia is the use of a word which by its very sound "makes" the meaning of the word. As many onomatopoetic words are used in prose and in daily speech as in poetry. "Hiss," "roar," "bang," "crash," "sigh," "clash," "rip," "mewing," "babble," and "plopping" are a few such words taken almost at random from poems in this book; you can think of dozens of others.

IV

METHODS OF PRESENTING IDEAS IN POETRY

1. *Figures of Speech*

Figures of speech (or *figures,* as they are often called for short) are indirect or arresting ways of presenting ideas.

Eight, the most common ones in English, are given below in alphabetical order.

a. *Apostrophe* is addressing a person who is dead or otherwise absent as if he were present. See "The Saint."

b. *Climax* is the building up of a poetic effect to a point of high interest. Both *climax* and its opposite, *anticlimax,* may be found in "Silhouette" and "Scum o' the Earth."

c. *Hyperbole* is exaggeration for effect. No one is expected to believe it; nevertheless it drives the point home, if it is not too extreme. See "The Horse Thief."

d. *Irony* comes from the Greek for "veil." It deceives no thoughtful reader, although the words state the exact opposite of what the poet means. See "Does It Matter?"

e. *Metaphor* is comparing two things without the use of *like* or *as.* The things must be unlike in all respects save the important one. Metaphors may be statements, as in the sestet of "Answer," or may lurk in one word, "This dwarfs our *emerald* country."

f. *Metonymy* is the use of one word for another closely associated with it. For example, "The sidewalk *bleachers* yelled as he / Speared a sizzler dizzily."

g. *Personification* is a development of metaphor. An inanimate thing or some form of life less than human is compared to a person, without the use of *like* or *as.* See "Highmount."

h. *Simile* is the most common of all these figures. By the use of *like* or *as* it compares two things unlike in all respects save the important one. See "Hills Ruddy with Sumach." A very good poem for showing the differences between metaphors and similes is "Wing Harbor."

2. The Imagists

The Imagists were a group of six poets (Amy Lowell and John Gould Fletcher are the two represented in this book) who in 1912 issued an anthology of their poems with a preface containing their poetic creed. Its articles are worth studying, and interesting to compare with the ones set forth by Wordsworth and Coleridge in the famous preface to *Lyrical Ballads*.

"1. To use the language of common speech, but to employ always the *exact* word, not the nearly exact, nor the merely decorative word.

"2. To create new rhythms—as the expression of new moods —and not to copy old rhythms, which merely echo old moods. We do not insist upon "free verse" as the only method of writing poetry. We fight for it as a principle of liberty. We believe that the individuality of a poet may often be better expressed in free-verse than in conventional forms. In poetry a new cadence means a new idea.

"3. To allow absolute freedom in the choice of subject. It is not good art to write badly of aeroplanes and automobiles, nor is it necessarily bad art to write well about the past. We believe passionately in the artistic value of modern life, but we wish to point out that there is nothing so uninspiring nor as old-fashioned as an aeroplane of the year 1911.

"4. To present an image (hence the name: 'Imagist'). We are not a school of painters, but we believe that poetry should render particulars exactly and not deal in vague generalities, however magnificent and sonorous. It is for this reason that we oppose the cosmic poet, who seems to us to shirk the responsibilities of his art.

"5. To produce poetry that is hard and clear, never blurred and indefinite.

"6. Finally, most of us believe that concentration is of the very essence of poetry."

3. Objective Method

When a poet tries to subordinate his own personality and views in presenting imaginary scenes, people, or situations, we say that he is writing objectively. Older English poetry—tales and ballads—is almost all objective.

See "The Creation," "Kansas Boy," "Cardigan Bay."

4. Subjective Method

When a poet consciously injects his own personality and views into a poem, the method becomes subjective. Most subjective poems are in the form of free lyrics or of sonnets. But stories may sometimes be told in such a way that we can never forget who is telling it. (See "The Saint.")

For subjective free lyrics see "Rencontre," "To an Athlete Dying Young," and the note on "Barter." For subjective sonnets see "The Soldier," "Definition," and "Answer."

5. Restraint

An old college professor's advice to young writers was, "When you are reading over what you have written and come to a passage that you think is particularly fine, *cut it out.*" If you can understand the reason for his advice and the reason for quoting it here, you will understand the theory of restraint in poetry. If you still do not believe in its effectiveness, read first some of Ella Wheeler Wilcox's poems, and then some of Emily Dickinson's. Most of the poems in this collection are on the restrained side; there are at least fourteen, however, which are quite unrestrained. Pick out some of them and test them for emotional effect. (Note: The college professor's advice was to *young* writers.)

6. Understatement

When a poet understates, he goes a step beyond restraint; he does not avail himself even of a legitimate show of emotion, but uses expressions which at first sight seem utterly inadequate. At the second and third reading, though, we begin to think about them—pretty hard.

See "Bare Feet." For a very effective combination of understatement with irony, see "Does It Matter?"

7. Cliché

The French use the word "cliché" for an electrotype plate, which, as you may know, is only a facsimile of the original, and yet the thing from which thousands of copies are made. The expression became transferred, very aptly, to words and phrases which have been used thousands of times to convey ideas. For flagrant examples, see the words of almost any popular song. Then turn to a poem where a very conscious attempt has been made to avoid clichés, "The Pylons."

INDEX OF AUTHORS

A

F

G

H

N

O

R

S

INDEX OF TITLES

A

B

C

296

H

I

K

L

M

N

O

P

R

S

T

U

W

INDEX OF FIRST LINES

W

Y